EARL K. LONG
AND
JAY CHEVALIER
"When the Music Stopped"

By

Jay Chevalier

Introduction
by
John Tarver

Artwork
by
Gail H. Shelton

SOUTHERN LEGACIES PRESS

132 Rue St. Denis
Natchitoches, LA 71457

2003

This volume is published by Southern Legacies Press and is the first in a series commemorating the Bicentennial celebration of the Louisiana Purchase. It is fitting that Southern Legacies Press is domiciled in Natchitoches, Louisiana, the oldest European permanent settlement in the Louisiana Purchase Territory.

Typeface is Adobe Garamond. Headlines 18 point type, bold. Body Text is 11 point type, leaded on 14 points.
Printer: Mid South Press, 850 Stoner Ave., Shreveport, Louisiana 71101
Binder: Universa! Bookbindery, 1200 N. Colorado, San Antonio, Texas 78207

Southern Legacies Press
132 Rue St. Denis
Natchitoches, Louisiana 71457-4636

Southern Legacies Press is a wholly owned subsidiary of Price Associates Incorporated

Dedication

This book is dedicated to my mother "Mama Jewell",
my father "Daddy Joe," my children Jan Dawn, Jay Earl, Cid Zane,
my wife Gisela, my sister Judie Jane,
her family Ray, Dana, Debra and Keith.

Mama Jewell, age 18
circa 1930

Contents

Acknowledgements

A special thanks to Ron Skains for his contribution to this book. Ron believed in the story and shepherded the project until it became the finished book. I would also like to thank Steve and Gail Shelton for their support above and beyond the canons of Southern courtesy, friendship and hospitality. The contribution Gail made to the book with her artwork is outstanding and helps visually tell the story.

John Tarver's introduction is an essay that captures the time and circumstance of Earl Long politics and explains the real essence of the complexities of Louisiana in 1959-1960. The introduction could stand alone as a real contribution to our politics and polemics as the Long era comes to a close in Louisiana.

I would also like to thank Gene Levine, Thelma and Dan Lupton, Carolyn Phillips, Michael Wynne, John Lutes, Board of Directors, staff and management of the Louisiana Political Hall of Fame. It is an honor to be inducted into the Hall of Fame. I would also like to acknowledge my second hometown, Winnfield, the citizens of Winn Parish, Mayor Deano Thornton, Claudell, Bill, Jimmy, and all my other "hog-dog" friends. Thanks also to Mr. Clem Huffman, Earl Long's original "side-kick."

Thanks to Pee Wee, my first song writing partner, Betty McGowan, my friends at Primerica, Sonny Wooley, Mary Rambo, movie director Ron Shelton, Alfred and Betty Lamson of Lafayette, Margaret Woodward and to all who made this book possible. To all the readers of this book, including Eugene Manuel of Mamou who placed the first order for a book, may you be blessed with a "long-shot" in your life.

Special thanks to Louisiana Secretary of State Fox McKeithen, Amy Allen, Lt. Governor Kathleen Blanco, internationally renowned author Jason Berry, West Virginia Secretary of State Joe Mansion, Huey and Jill Perry, Jim Engster, host of the "Louisiana Live" network and Blaze Starr of Huntington, West Virginia. I would like to thank the staff of Southern Legacies Press, Carol Wells, former editor of the Northwestern State University Press, Carol Lann and Sherry Heflin of Mid South Press for the finished book.

This book has been a labor of love, passion and honor to the memory of Governor Earl K. Long.

Preface

Jay Chevalier was born in Lecompte, Louisiana on the banks of Bayou Boeuf. His mother, Jewell, and father, Joe, realized that she was pregnant at a July 4th Huey P. Long political rally on Spring Creek, near Glenmora, Louisiana when she developed the first signs of morning sickness. Maybe it was a premonition of things to come.

At the brink of World War II, Jay's family was as poor as the proverbial church mouse. His grandfather had been killed in a logging accident in the Louisiana cypress swamps. This tragedy left Jay's paternal grandmother alone to support four tiny children by chopping wood and selling goat meat to others who were more fortunate.

Jay's dad fought valiantly with the Navy in several major campaigns of World War II in the South Pacific, including the Battle of Okinawa on Easter Sunday in 1945. The war caused his dad to leave Jay, his mother, and a six-month-old sister, Judie Jane, alone in the piney wood hills outside of Forest Hill, Louisiana for two frightening years. When his dad finally came home, Jay heard stories of the war that were swapped by his father with a neighbor, Mr. Leo Hearn, who had also been in the Navy. These stories instilled a burning desire in this 10-year-old boy's heart to see the world and to help lift himself and his family from the poverty he'd been born into.

The Saturday night picture shows offered the best examples of escape. The cowboy heroes glittered and galloped across the local movie screens, playing their guitars and singing hero songs of the great, golden Wild West. Gene Autry was most influential on young Jay. Pretty soon, he had a Sears Roebuck guitar and a dream of fame and fortune. This dream led him right to the Governor of Louisiana in 1959 with a hit song he had written, entitled, "The Ballad of Earl K. Long." The Governor had just escaped from two mental institutions, and his antics were making headlines, nationally and internationally.

This notoriety did not bother the young guitar picker from the piney woods. No sir, for he was swept up on a tide of publicity, and the glitter was too much to resist. The song became so popular you could drive from Shreveport to New Orleans and catch the beginning, the middle, or end of the catchy tune by just pressing each push button on your car radio. It sold over a 100,000 copies and had everyone clapping and singing along, even if they hadn't voted for Uncle Earl. It landed him his own room at the Louisiana Governor's mansion, plus a $200-per-week campaign-singing salary, then unheard of. Most importantly, this book is an eyewitness account of the last "glory" days of one of our nation's most colorful Governors and Louisiana's own favorite son.

Earl Kemp Long, the political heir of the Huey P. Long empire was Governor of Louisiana three different times; a feat no one before him in Louisiana history attained. His accomplishments as Governor helped launch Louisiana forward from a swamp kingdom and into the modern day twentieth century. The Longs of Louisiana literally paved the way for their constituents to join the mainstream of American life. Until they came along, there were very few hard-surfaced roads or bridges leading across the bayous and rivers from the swampy south of the state to the piney wood hills of north Louisiana.

The Longs' innovation of free school books, paper, and pencils for each student, plus free hot lunches for the poor and underprivileged child, was a milestone for the nation. The old age pension for the elderly endeared many a heart to the Longs. Earl was the architect of this pension, and to this day is fondly remembered as "The best friend the poor white man and colored ever had."

His last days were exciting, colorful, miraculous, and red hot! They just added fire to the legend, a fire that still has not burned out. If fanned just a little, that fire burns brighter than a gas flare on a Louisiana oil well derrick.

In the spring of 1989, the Long fire was fanned one more time by none other than Paul Newman playing the part of Earl K. Long in a Touchstone movie filmed in Louisiana, entitled, "Blaze."

This book, Earl K. Long and Jay Chevalier is intended to keep the flame burning brightly long after the curtain comes down at the last picture show.

* * *

Earl K. Long hated his wife, Blanche and his nephew, Russell Long until the day he died in September of 1960. How could you forgive anyone who had committed you to two different mental institutions within the same month? He loved little children (especially orphans), common people (both black and white), Catholics, Protestants, Cajuns, Louisiana, a New Orleans stripper, and a country music guitar picker! They embraced him, his ideas, his courage, his vulnerabilities, and his dreams of a modern-day Louisiana that would be a better place for everyone to live in. He had a passion for buttermilk, cornbread, hoop cheese, sardines, onions, crackers, peaches, and all kinds of fruit. He had a permanent suite at the world-famous Roosevelt Hotel in New Orleans, an apartment at the Pentagon Barracks in Baton Rouge, and owned an old, tin-roofed farmhouse with 160 acres of land he liked to call his "Pea Patch" farm. The farm was located on the outskirts of Winnfield, Louisiana, his birthplace. He spent equal time at all three places in the last few months of his life, as he stumped the Eighth District of Louisiana, seeking to unseat the political enemy. He was also trying to regain the power he had lost through the manipulations of his wife, nephew, former political allies, and a few overly anxious friends who thought he had gone crazy and was all washed up.

He won! Then lost to that old grim reaper. Actually, he lived nine bittersweet days of victory, then death cheated him from seeing his dream come true. He died with a curse on his lips for his enemies and a hope in his heart for the soon-to-be President John F. Kennedy. He somehow knew JFK was going to be elected, even though his first choice would have been Stuart Simington of Missouri. Two days before his death, he was planning to stump the South for Kennedy, free of charge. Surely, Camelot would have been much stronger with a Louisiana Long on the team and in the court.

His last election helped ignite a glimmer of hope for the black man's integration into southern society. This was a bold statement for a politician to make; for Earl K. Long was the first Southerner to recognize publicly that integration was going to happen, even though it was politically unpopular. His foes used this to help cast him in the role of a crazy person. Earl K. Long and John F. Kennedy both saw the future in their mind's eye, but neither lived to live it. However, the world, Louisiana and America are better places because they once passed this way.

Life with the Governor was like a tragicomedy. He always raced the wind. Twenty-hour days were common and sometimes they stretched to twenty-four and forty-eight. His stamina was legendary. He could and would wear down an entourage of ten men. There was never a dull moment with Earl! Some moments were sad, some moments were funny. The end was both.

We have so little to do with our births or deaths. The man who meticulously prepares for his demise is no more in control than the one who is felled by the assassin's bullet or a heart attack. The one who writes his will, leaves explicit instructions for the funeral arrangements, i.e. songs, no open casket, graveside services only, and what relatives and friends get the money. The other flagrantly tackles life as if there is no tomorrow. He seeks today's rewards, giving no heed to eternity, as if that is left to a higher power who will judge us all with or without preparation for one's death. The mourners file by either's casket, muttering words of praise and condolences to both acquaintances and relatives alike. For death is the great equalizer! It is the boundary where the living cannot follow nor the corpse return from; therefore, kind words issue forth as if there had been no enmity in life.

Only the bereaved friend can tell the difference, wishing in their heart to either have taken the place of the departed or vowing to avenge the injustices of this life at a future date. Such vows or thoughts in the cold light of day either vanish with time, leaving history to write a distorted picture, or spring forth from the devoted heart, years later, to tell a new generation and some remnants of the old that "Something is rotten in the state of Denmark." (From Hamlet, Act I)

I met the Governor just a few days after his 64th birthday. Neither of us suspected he'd be dead in less than a year. He was a much older experienced man in a hurry. I was wrapped up in a youthful ambition, also in a hurry. I have since learned through experience to beware of someone who is in such a hurry because their demise usually not far off. With unbelievable strength of will and purpose, they hurdle through their remaining time here on earth, sweeping everyone around them toward and through unfinished tasks and goals. Some, like the Governor, go out in a blaze of glory, leaving behind burned bridges, burned-out comrades, and a burning question unanswered; what if he had lived. . . lived just a little longer?

Hindsight is 20/20. This story is about the way it was as we climbed then stood on top of that last great political mountain of the Long Dynasty in Louisiana in September of 1960. I know it's true, because of the 360 and some-odd days I lived and eye-witnessed these events and was there "when the music stopped."

* * *

What do I hope to accomplish by writing <u>Earl K. Long and Jay Chevalier</u>? To make excuses for Earl or to vindicate Earl? No. There are some things that cannot be excused. Like the time he streaked the second floor of the Roosevelt Hotel or urinated in a large potted plant in the hotel lobby. However, I will explain the circumstances, which are very humorous and *very* Earl K. Long. History alone will vindicate him.

After so many years of silence, what do I hope to say or accomplish that's different from any other writer? Frankly, I'm going to fulfill a silent promise I made to myself and to his spirit as I stood at the back of a throng of people in Winnfield, Louisiana, September, 1961. The occasion was the unveiling of a monument to Earl, and on the speaker's rostrum were relatives, former political allies, plus various other dignitaries. As hot tears ran down my cheeks, someone next to me said, "Jay, you deserve to be up there more than anyone else on that stand. You were loyal to the end."

While it was true that I had become closer than anyone to Earl in the last few months he lived, my absence from the rostrum was not what was bothering me. The people on the platform were paying homage to a legacy that had started with Earl's brother, Huey. Every damn one of them on the rostrum had high stakes in the Louisiana political legend. It was politically expedient that they promote and perpetuate the Long legacy, not only for their aggrandizement, but also if they didn't stick together under a smoke screen of unity, some of them might wind up in jail. So it wasn't their facade that bothered me – nor me not being up on the speaker's rostrum. No. It was the fact that almost to a man or woman each one of them had either double-crossed or despised him; or jumped the political ship when it looked like Earl was sinking in the first primary of his last campaign; or they had stolen money from him.

The tragedy is that Earl knew this in his last days, and he had come to grips with it. What angered me was that these same double-crossers were mouthing words of great praise about a man some of them had betrayed and said was crazy, and even had committed to a mental institution. So what was my silent promise? Simply stated, I swore silently to tell Earl's side of the story, someday.

Why did I wait so long? First of all, it was too emotionally traumatic for me to do immediately after Earl's death. Secondly, it was a long time before I could look at all the facts with a rational eye. An example of this: I was Earl's bodyguard and aide-de-camp in those last, emotion-packed days. My first reaction to his death was to check my loaded .38, for I was sure he had been killed. My first thought was, who do I kill first? Finally, time, plus my own experiences in life, have made me much more capable of writing his side of the story as it actually happened that last year of his life.

Introduction

A woman of a certain age entered a voting booth in rural Ouachita Parish during the 1960 primary Congressional election in Louisiana, but a few minutes later her head popped out of the privacy curtain on the voting machine: "Where's Earl Long?" she demanded. She had voted for Earl Long every time he ran for office and planned to do so again. Precinct workers explained that the former governor was a candidate for Congress in the Eighth Congressional District, a hundred miles to the south. In Ouachita Parish, then in the Fifth Congressional District, Otto Passman was unopposed for re-election to Congress. Mr. Passman, colleagues said, was so nervous he wore his clothes out from the inside, but he seldom had an opponent and by 1960 had never lost an election. It was an understandable error; after all, Earl Long had never run for anything less extensive than a statewide office. The woman left the polls disappointed.

Earl Long had no such perfect record as Otto Passmen. By 1960 he had won three and lost three statewide elections. Now he was back in Central Louisiana running for the seat in Congress occupied by brother George Long until 1958. A young Alexandria lawyer, Harold McSween, had won the seat two years earlier and presented himself now for re-election. Earl Long challenged him. The subsequent race, a traditional stump campaign, boiled down to a referendum on Earl Long's 30-plus years of public service, beginning with his patronage job as the attorney to assist the inheritance tax collector in New Orleans in 1928.

In 1960 as wire editor of the Monroe Morning World, the daily newspaper serving Ouachita Parish and surrounding parishes, on weekends I presided over the teletype machine, used normally for transmitting state, national and international news stories and photographs. But the teletype also served to keep our city editor in touch with other editors around the state. The Morning World was one of the chain of newspapers, along with the New Orleans States and the Shreveport Times, founded by Col. Robert Ewing of New Orleans, the man credited with virtually creating Huey Long, who once in office denounced his benefactor and built a political base of his own; Colonel Ewing and the Ewing family never forgave the Longs. That Saturday night, the teletype chattered constantly with an extended conversation between Bill Bailey, city editor of the Alexandria Daily Town Talk, and our own Dallas Roper. Mr. Bailey planned an office party in Alexandria once Earl Long lost the Congressional race to Harold McSween, and Mr. Roper, presumably with other editors around the state, hoped to join in the festivities. Early returns from Alexandria, the district's only city, gave McSween, its native son, a commanding lead, but by late evening the country vote overwhelmed the hopes of journalists, who despised the populism of Earl Long. By 11:00 p.m. the teletype chatter had virtually ceased, and we heard from Mr. Bailey no more that evening. Earl Long had won, and the "lying newspapers" retired to Mudville.

Little more than a week later Earl Long died. Because the election was only a party primary, it was left to the District Central Committee of the Democratic Party to name a candidate to replace Earl Long on the general election ballot. The committee voted with only one member dissenting (Judge John Pickett of Sabine Parish who, ironically, had begun his career by supporting Sam Jones for Governor against Earl Long) to place Harold McSween on the ballot as the Democratic candidate for Congress and incidentally condemning McSween to defeat by another Long two years later. (That Long would suffer defeat by still another Long two years hence.) In that day, a place on the Democratic ballot was tantamount to election, despite the Constitutional requirement that members of the House of Representatives be popularly elected. That was Judge Pickett's point, one that Governor Jones would doubtless have approved and Earl Long, had he been alive, would have savored..

In this memoir, Jay Chevalier recounts his own experiences with Earl Long in the failed race for Lieutenant Governor in 1959 and the successful race for Democrat nomination to Congress in 1960. In the process he solves a mystery, propounded by the late television and motion picture producer Brooks Read, who covered Governor Long for Baton Rouge broadcast media. How, he asked, could so many people have crowded into Earl Long's sickroom to see him die? If all the people who claimed to have been at Earl Long's bedside at that moment were collected in the same place, it would surely have taken a football field to hold them all. Jay Chevalier sets the record straight. He had gone to his parents' home in Forest Hill about 20 miles from Alexandria the evening of Earl Long's death, leaving an illiterate "gofer" to watch over the Congressman-elect. It was a fitting end for the man who courted and claimed the allegiance of the little man.

But this is not the principal theme of Jay Chevalier's story. Because he juxtaposes Earl Long's efforts to rebuild his political credibility alongside Jay Chevalier's own efforts to establish validity in Country music, we may safely infer that this memoir posits politics as a form of popular entertainment - or vice versa. By the time this account starts Governor Long had suffered a sharp decline in public support. He had publicly exhibited grotesque eccentricities occasioned by dementia associated with heart disease, which led him through the mental health wards of at least three hospitals. For his part, Jay Chevalier had not yet demonstrated even the rudimentary talents necessary for success as a musician. What could possibly have drawn together this washed-up political antediluvian and this raw young musical tyro? In a vivid account that breathes authenticity - sometimes maudlin, sometimes obscene, but always vigorous - Country singer and song writer Jay Chevalier tells us. By inference, he also asks: Why did politics after Earl Long lose its color and excitement and retreat into a gray bureaucratic fog?

The easiest answer may be found in Governor Long's illness; his friends said he was just tired, but his political enemies answered that he was just plain crazy, and always had been. There is some support for the latter. Members of the Long family, for example, blame Earl Long's defeat for re-election in 1959 on an unfortunate comparison he drew in a stump speech in deep north Louisiana between the state's school teachers and the world's oldest profession. It was vintage Earl Long on the stump, but it carried a harsh unforgiving edge in the next day's newspapers. One could argue that no politician in his right mind would denounce teachers, most of whom were women, as whores because they had demanded a pay increase.

Although Governor Long's health problems twenty years later certainly may have contributed to his bizarre political antics, they do not explain his lifelong tendency to fall out and fight with those nearest and dearest, including his wife Blanche Revere Long, his brothers Julius, George and Huey, his benefactor (and owner of two of the most powerful broadcast stations in the state) Governor James A. Noe, his boyhood friend and political counselor Senator A.A. Fredericks, his hand-picked ticket to succeed him as leaders of the state Judge Carlos Spaght and Public Service Commissioner John J. McKeithen, his nephew Sentor Russell Long, his cousin Senator Speedy O. Long, and scores of others. In their places of esteem and camaraderie, Governor Long often substituted characters from the extremes of Louisiana's multi-factional politics. A good example of the latter was Joe Arthur Sims, along with his father, Professor Linus Sims, a dyed-in-the-wood Anti-Long during the Richard Lesche-Earl Long regime of the late 1930s. Their political heavy-handedness, the Sims family blamed for the loss of the senior Mr. Sims's position as president of Southeast Louisiana State College in Hammond, and within a few weeks his position as professor at the Louisiana State Normal College in Natchitoches. By the time Jay Chevalier's story begins in the 1950s, however, the younger Mr. Sims had become Earl Long's attorney and close political associate. At some point in the intervening years Governor Long had made his peace with the Sims family, as he did time and again with his former political opponents. His former associates faded into the background. Joe Arthur Sims responded by putting in place and carrying out the plan to free Governor Long from the Southeast Louisiana Mental Hospital in Mandeville in 1959. When Mr. Sims finally got access to his client and joined him in his hospital room, Earl Long exclaimed: "Joe Arthur, where the hell you been?" In subsequent campaigns, Mr. Sims played straight-man to Governor Long, warming up the crowds on the stump and introducing the candidates and other speakers. Several years later Mr. Sims toyed with the idea of seeking statewide office on the strength of his association with the late Governor but gave it up. It would have been an anticlimax after the legal legerdemain he had demonstrated on behalf of the imprisoned Governor. An elected office would not have added anything to his indelible reputation as the lawyer who broke Earl Long out of the insane asylum.

For his final bid for statewide office in 1959, Earl Long ran for Lieutenant

Governor on a ticket headed by his old friend James A. Noe. Governor Noe's ticket included, in addition to Earl Long, Curt Siegelin, a candidate for secretary of state; Ben Bennett for attorney general; Pat Tugwell for state treasurer; Bobby Dugas for comptroller; Sidney McCrory for commissioner of agriculture and immigration; Wayne Gaudin for register of state lands; Edgar Coco for insurance commissioner; and Douglas Fowler for custodian of voting machines. The Democratic primary election fell on December 5, and the general election the next month. Only Pat Tugwell, a veteran of more than 30 years in the office, and Douglas Fowler, a gray bureaucrat, won election. Political tickets had become old fashioned by 1959, and four years later would be reduced to bobtail tickets, usually candidates for governor and lieutenant governor. By 1967 tickets had vanished, and each candidate mounted his own campaign.

"By Their Deeds Ye Shall Know Them," the Noe-Long campaign literature proclaimed in 1959, adding:

> When Earl K. Long ran for Governor on two previous occasions, certain newspapers and anti-Long politicians did everything in their power to make the people believe him to be dishonest. When these anti-Long "Reformers" [read, Sam Jones Administration] were elected to office, they investigated everything in his public and private life to try to find something that might be misrepresented as proof of their false campaign charges. They found nothing, despite examining all aspects of every administration in which he served. Instead, the result of all Federal and State investigations proved that the vile insinuations and charges of the anti-Long politicians, and their propaganda mouth-pieces were unfounded and untrue.
>
> Earl Long has been talked about, criticized and slandered more than any other public figure of our State by a certain segment of the press and these so-called anti-Long politicians. They talk of machine politics, when they have built up the biggest, most ruthless payroll-political machine [read, deLesseps Morrison mayoral administration] in the history of the City of New Orleans. They talk about peace and harmony [read, Jimmie Davis campaign's theme], yet some of the most difficult times for the people of this State have occurred when the do-nothings were in office.
>
> In the present term they [read, Ms. Blanche and Russell Long] have tried to hold up the candidate for Lieutenant Governor on this ticket as being crazy, deranged, a drunkard, a roughneck, and a man whose personal conduct is such that it is reprehensible insofar as the ladies of this State and others are concerned.
>
> Earl Long has said time and time again that he would rather have the respect and appreciation, the warmth of heart and good will of the good peo-

ple of this State than to be the richest man in the whole world. The Holy Bible says that greed is one of the worst afflictions man can possess.....

We bear no malice toward anyone. We will have no enemies to punish when this election is at an end. Our only ambition is to give the people of Louisiana the kind of government that will benefit all the people, instead of just a handful.

With all routes to political power at the state level effectively closed to Earl Long, he now turned his attention to national politics. To understand Governor Long and his responses to his political environment, one must study the cast of political characters of the time; neither Earl Long nor indeed any politician can operate in a vacuum. In most cases, each character represented an independent political position in the churning gumbo of Louisiana politics. None of them could logically or for long be described as completely beholden to Earl Long; none would dare admit to permanent membership in a distinct political faction within the dominant Democratic Party; each exhibited and exercised a political independence that belies journalists' charges of cronyism. This constantly evolving political landscape permitted Earl Long to fashion and refashion his political prospects.

Earl K. Long and Jay Chevalier, "When the Music Stopped", then, serves as both a political and musical memoir, and it often seems each account outdoes the other in brass. Of course, the very act of self-promotion requires an egregious egoism when no altruism informs it. Jay Chevalier takes great pains to demonstrate his disinterest, the governor with his public service and Jay Chevalier his art, behind his and Earl Long's efforts to gain popular acceptance. Each in his own way extended the folk myth of American democracy, operating at the very base level of popular communications. The political stump on which they performed, however, would not long survive Governor Long. It gave way in a few short years to the electronic media, to political consultants, to sound bites and video tape. In Jay Chevalier's account the gorge rises, the kind that chokes, from the inevitable loss of contact, even rapport, between entertainers-cum-politicians and their public. Governor Long cannot escape the harsh light of the television camera.

Even today, those with any pretensions to political sophistication have a favorite Earl Long story; Jay Chevalier has scores of them. He writes from personal observation, while many other yarns about Earl Long are apocryphal, at best; the Governor called them "vile insinuations." Because of the disparity in their ages, more than forty years, Jay Chevalier limits his account to Governor Long's last few years and his final two races for public office, in which the author played a not-inconsiderable part. At the same time the lure of a musical career troubled the younger man, while it beckoned to him with promises of fame and fortune, fueling a fierce yearning that matched the Governor's yearning for another political office. Both the politician and the singer ignored the voices of caution, of reason, and plunged into the maelstrom of partisan politics.

In 1939 in Governor Long's unsuccessful effort to hold onto office against the challenge of Sam Houston Jones, some of the latter's adherents accused Earl Long of hog stealing, in that day a most powerful and provocative charge that carried an onus only slightly less offensive than a charge of miscegenation. It was a dangerous tactic, adopted with caution and with a sure knowledge of its consequences. It could not have escaped the notice of the Jones camp that only four years earlier, Senator Huey Long's descent into racial politics had resulted in his murder. Fortunately, it never came to that again. I was eight years old that winter, but I recall vividly the outrage of many of our neighbors at the audacity of "High Hat" Sam Jones and his menials. At his parish seat political meetings, Sam Jones took the reference in good humor, when a local supporter invariably presented him with a stovepipe hat in recognition of the slur. I was grown before I learned the basis of the hog-stealing charge, and iron-ically from Governor Jones himself. Long after the race had ended in a Jones victo-ry, the U.S. Attorney in Shreveport released a report exonerating Governor Long on the question of profits from the sale of hogs by state institutions, including sales by the Normal College at Natchitoches, where Sen. A.A. Fredericks served as president. In that day, prisons and colleges were expected to feed themselves, which explains their traffic in hogs.

This moving portrait of Earl Long revealed in scores of mostly amusing stories, recounting his eccentricities and foibles, pose a problem for the biographer. Jay Chevalier, because of his time-frame, the limited time during which he knew Governor Long, holds with the description of the Governor published by LSU's Waldo Braden in The Oral Tradition in the South (LSU, 1983):

> No one fit the stereotype of a "good ole country boy" better than this disheveled old man, with his folksy speech and his gravel voice. He often appeared on the stump coatless, wearing an old pair of baggy tan pants held up by galluses, sometimes with only one fastened, and a badly wrinkled, sweaty white shirt, open at the collar and bagging halfway out of his pants.... Hanging carelessly out of a back pocket or waving in his hand was his favorite colored bandanna, with which he casually mopped his sweaty face while talking.

Dr. Braden's description comes directly out of the "lying newspapers" in 1959 and 1960. Had he looked further into the past he would have found starkly different descriptions of the man. His widow once told me her husband as a young man in New Orleans, a meticulous dresser - almost a dandy - did not trust anyone, not even Mrs. Long, to care for his clothes. He affected tailored business suits and hats. The testimony of Sheriff Hebert of St. John the Baptist Parish supports Mrs. Long's account. Several years after the Governor died the Sheriff described to me the bachelor Earl Long dressed one morning complete with carnation in his lapel, driving his new Studebaker roadster out of the Monteleone Hotel parking garage into the traffic of the Vieux Carre on his way to elope with the beautiful Blanche Revere; Ms. Blanche was indeed a beautiful young woman. Sheriff Hebert, a state motorcycle policeman in the late 1920s, which was a patronage job dependent on Gov. Huey Long's whim, feared for his job, which consisted in large part in his riding herd on the Governor's younger brother, at that time a grown man about thirty years old, to keep him out of trouble that might embarrass the Administration. Posted at the exit of the garage with his motorcycle, Sheriff Hebert thought nothing of Earl Long driving his automobile to the local service station apparently for gasoline, but this time to Hebert's surprise and chagrin the Governor's little brother left with the wife of the service station owner. Earl Long and Blanche Revere were married after the divorce. It would not be the last time police and medical personnel failed to contain the free spirit of Earl Long. The marriage survived unusual upheavals in the rough and tumble of an active political life until Governor Long took sick and within the year died estranged from his wife.

In his earlier political contests, beginning in 1932 when Earl Long first ran for statewide office, in this case for lieutenant governor, he invariably dressed in a dark business suit and wore a conservatively blocked wool hat, the enduring symbol of the Southern working man. In summer in Baton Rouge and New Orleans he sported white seersucker suits and white or two-toned shoes. In the 1948 race, Earl Long and his ticket appeared in our village, as they did in virtually every community in the state. The candidates spoke from the high verandah under the false front of our general store. It was late in the campaign, in the fall, and Earl Long wore a dark suit and overcoat under a gray snap-brim hat. He attempted to speak, but he had nearly lost his voice, so all we heard was a deep growl. It did not matter, because virtually all the voters wanted was for him to show up. In this race Earl Long did not play the clown. That was left to Senator Jimmie Morrison of Hammond who stumped the state accompanied by a monkey that he addressed as Earl Long. In our village the vast majority of our people voted for Earl Long, some of whom did so to send a message to "Monkey" Morrison. By 1959 when he again ran for lieutenant governor, the political dress code had begun to change, as it had that for entertainers. Earl Long and Jay Chevalier simply followed a trend toward the informal.

Earl Long did in fact portray himself as a "good ole country boy," although he had made New Orleans his home since he was a boy. What's more, his upbringing in Winnfield, a country town with a growing industrial proletariat, did not support the image he projected from the stump. He was born in 1895 into a family of prosperous upland farmers, lawyers, and bankers. In a day when most boys of the region left school in the primary grades, Earl Long completed high school and undergraduate college at Louisiana Tech and Louisiana State. At LSU he was a classmate of Freddie Fredericks and Sam Jones, until poverty drove Sam to leave college to read law in DeRidder, his hometown. Earl Long's college record earned him a scholarship to Loyola University Law School in New Orleans where he trained for the bar. Three of his brothers also became lawyers, one also a dentist; his sisters attended normal schools, and one of them earned an advanced degree at Columbia University in New York. His father, Pierce Long, lived the life of a planter, letting out his arable lands to share croppers, mostly white families, and dabbled in real estate, principally timber lands. Pierce's brother Frank served as president of a local bank. After Earl Long graduated law school and passed the bar, he found employment in New Orleans. The insular urban life of the Crescent City fitted him well, and he developed typically urban traits, particularly a passion for betting on horse races.

Those who knew Earl Long well stressed his unusual prejudices. He never trusted a man, for example, who counted his change after he paid a bar tab; the practice betrayed a love of money. He also rated his friends by their willingness to pick up a bar tab. His protege, John McKeithen, who would parlay his acquaintance with Earl Long into two terms in the governor's office, was not known for openhandedness. The young McKeithen acted, Earl Long said, like he had fish hooks in his pocket. As the state's chief administrator, Earl Long avoided paying high salaries to those he appointed to unclassified jobs. One should never pay a man more than he was used to getting because, he said, most people simply cannot stand prosperity.

Jay Chevalier's memoir is not the first to point out Earl Long's verbal crudities. Indeed, his yarns and political hyperbole from the stump includes a form of scatological humor that runs through popular discourse, particularly in the South, from the early national period. Mark Twain, for example, and his contemporary, Jefferson Davis, peppered their public speeches with dead cats and tumble bugs, among other unsavory subjects. LSU's Bill Cooper quotes Davis in a new biography of the Confederate president (Knopf, 2000): "...the Whig Party claim to be the decency Party, raise their coons and roll their balls, but they remind me of a certain insect which rolls its ball backward and down hill." Dean Cooper in a footnote attributes the term, "coon," to Democrats who used it to describe Whigs, which is correct as far as it goes. Of course it misses the point Davis sought to make, that Whig planters were content to keep to their landed seats and raise their illegitimate offspring by their slave women. The image, reminiscent of much southwestern humor of the period, of "a certain insect" alludes to the tumble bug, a beetle that rolls the dung of animals into balls that it buries in the ground after laying its eggs in them. Along with the ubiquitous pissant, one of Earl Long's favorite pejoratives, the tumble bug was a useful creature in a day when livestock crowded the public places. Although treated universally as an outcast, the tumble bug traveled country lanes and city streets alike. The pissant, very small and insignificant even for an ant, got its common name from the smell of formic acid associated with it; the root word, of course, is onomatopoetic. In any event, Earl Long used terms such as these in good company; the word appears in a range of classical writers, as well as the Wyclif and King James Bibles.

Such small traits, of course, cannot long sustain the reputation of public men. In our collective memory, it seems Earl Long occupies an empty stage. Indeed, how many of us who remember Governor Long can remember his opponents? Or even those candidates, and there were many of them, who actually defeated Governor Long? Earl Long was forced by his brother, the Governor, to withdraw his candidacy for lieutenant governor in 1932, then Richard Lesche outmaneuvered him for the Democratic nomination for governor in 1936. Earl Long settled for lieutenant governor that year and succeeded to the governor's office in 1939 when Governor Lesche resigned and went to prison for public theft. Sam Jones defeated Earl Long at the polls in 1940, but in turn lost to him in 1948. Governor Jones held no elective office before or after his one term. Jimmie Davis kept Earl Long in political exile until 1948 and returned to defeat him in 1960, then lived another forty years to celebrate his hundredth birthday. Robert Kennon took the governor's office from Earl Long's handpicked Spaght-McKeithen ticket in 1952. Kennon had been an appeals court judge, but he never won political office again, even falling victim to Earl Long protege John McKeithen's drive for the governor's office in 1964. Only the few specialists in local and state history in Louisiana's colleges care at all about these public figures, but Earl Long still holds a warm place in our public memory, I suspect as much for his weaknesses and foibles as for his long public service.

Jay Chevalier's memoir is only marginally political; his purpose is to account for his success as a Country singer and song writer, which he enjoyed over the intervening years largely because of his association with Earl Long as the Governor's musical biographer. The result was a string of ballads and "heart songs." Earl Long hired him to provide musical accompaniment for his race for lieutenant governor in 1959, on the strength of his record of "The Ballad of Earl K. Long," which he also wrote. Afterward he competed in contests, went out to Hollywood, followed the honkytonk circuit, and kept writing songs. It was a well-worn path; another Louisiana singer-song writer, the legendary Huddie (Leadbelly) Ledbedder followed a similar pattern, except that Leadbelly met Louisiana's Governor from the state penitentiary where he was serving a long sentence for attempted murder. Popular myth has Leadbelly gaining release from Angola State Penitentiary by entertaining Governor O.K. Allen with his rendition of black folk songs. It appears now, however, that the convict singer was simply paroled for good behavior. The record shows that earlier he did, indeed, sing his way out of the Texas state pen, despite his conviction for murder, a tribute to the power of music in politics. In the scheme of things, Jay Chevalier's musical contributions to Earl Long's stump performances were not out of place.

In 1960 Jay Chevalier returned to the campaign trail in Earl Long's campaign, this time in the Eighth Congressional District in central Louisiana, against incumbent Harold McSween, a scholarly lawyer with considerable histrionic talents of his own. The two campaigns crossed paths from time to time, and the two candidates engaged in mutual recriminations: "Shame on you, Harold McSween!" "Shame on you, Earl Long!" The great unwashed enjoyed nothing so much as a mud slinging contest, and they were not disappointed.

The Eighth Congressional District consisted then of the parishes of Avoyelles, Grant, LaSalle, Natchitoches, Rapides, Sabine, Vernon and Winn, an area that adopted Democratic, Populist, Socialist, and New Deal persuasions, and the heartland of the Long faction. It was an area in which Earl Long and his brothers Huey and George consistently ran well ahead of other candidates. Other Longs - either by blood or persuasion - continued long afterward to dominate the political landscape. After the 1990 Census Louisiana lost one of its eight seats in Congress, and the voters and territory of the former Eighth District were redistributed to the remaining seven districts; it destroyed the Long heartland.

Jay Chevalier takes his readers through Earl Long's last two campaigns, both of which had been conducted from the political stump, an antiquated practice even in the 1950s. It functioned much like an old-fashioned circus, with advance men, billboards, handbills, barkers, and confidence men. Both Earl Long and Jay Chevalier persisted, however, probably because they needed the reinforcement live audiences provided. Earl Long was too old and set in his ways to learn the new electronic system of campaigning, and Jay Chevalier was too young and inexperienced to command a more sophisticated audience. In the process, young Jay Chevalier learned about the political world, its perks, and its dangers. Earl Long dubbed him "the po' man's Jimmie Davis," a description that, while apt, somehow diminished the young musician's image. From Earl Long's last campaign, Jay Chevalier launched his singing and song writing career and developed enough self confidence to write about the experience with pity and compassion and no small part of admiration for an old man literally dying on his feet.

More than forty years have passed since the events of 1959-1960 and we can now look back on Earl Long and his world with some magnanimity. The memoir offered by balladeer Jay Chevalier has saved for us Earl Long in his native habitat; the gambler-oil man Glen Lowe, the Zwolle Tamale, Mr. Fredham Fredericks, the turncoat Dick Davis, China Berry Chickens and Dominicker Hens, Blaze Starr and Ms. Blanche, high- and low-brows, various denizens of the French Quarter, and a host of others who made up their political world.

John Tarver
Baton Rouge
January 2003

Chapter I

"Stranded"

A wise man once said, "The world steps aside for any man who knows where he is going." Well, I knew where I was going all right, to the Governor's mansion in Baton Rouge. But how was I to get there with a broken down Ford?

As darkness fell over me standing alone beside US Highway 190, little did I know that not only would Governor Earl K. Long step aside but cronies, troopers, strippers, and people in high places would too! I had the fire and the Governor held the match. Tonight the tinder or kindling would ignite in a blaze that's still burning.

Baton Rouge

A soft, September rain fell on my bare head as I stuck my thumb up in the darkness, trying to hail the oncoming headlights. Swoosh! The car went by, not even slowing, as all of the others had done for the past thirty minutes. The Brylcream hair tonic was slowly trickling down the back of my neck and around my ears, as the rain picked up its lazy Louisiana tempo on the guitar case at my feet by the side of the road. How in the hell did I come to be stranded on the side of the road anyway? This was crazy. I'd never hitchhiked in my twenty-three years of young life, not even when I was in the Marine Corps. I had always figured out a way to ride. This was truly crazy. The two-piece light-blue wool suit I was wearing began to stink as only wet wool can. It was repulsive to my nostrils. I was beginning to wish I'd stayed in the motel room in Melville in south central Louisiana. Even though Irma was drunk, and I didn't like the smell of used Vodka, at least her bed was warm and dry.

Maybe this was a bad idea anyway, I thought as I reached inside my coat pocket to feel the two purple and gold tickets that the Governor had just given me back in Melville. What had he said?

"Hell, tomorrow's when we need you. . . We'll be down in Cajun country, and you know how those Cajuns like music. . . Here's two tickets to the LSU/TCU football game tonight. . . Come go to the ball game and spend the night with us at the mansion."

Damn, that's what he said, as he drove off, leaving me standing in the middle of Main Street in Melville. As I looked at the two tickets, I had wondered whether to go on now, or stop by Irma's room for a drink. Irma won! How had all of this started anyway? For as long as I could remember, I had a burning desire to be a Country music entertainer. There was an ache down in my soul that could only be satisfied with applause after performing before a crowd of excited fans. Hell, it didn't make any difference where the crowd came from, as long as they applauded for me. For the last two days, the applause had come from Earl K. Long political audiences. For the last two weeks, I had been trying to get other paying jobs. I had the Number One song in Louisiana, "THE BALLAD OF EARL K. LONG," and no one would hire me because they thought it was just political and that I had been hired to write it for old Uncle Earl.

Truth was, I had been going to Louisiana College in Pineville, on the G.I. Bill for the last year and half, trying to figure out some way to break into the professional Country music entertainment business. In 1959, this was next to impossible. Elvis and Rock-a-billy were the big things happening. Yep, Rock 'n Roll had put us would-be country music entertainers on the backburner. It was so bad that some of the boys in Nashville had gotten together to form a new organization called CMA - Country Music Association. It probably wouldn't amount to a damn thing, I thought. It sure wouldn't help a struggling, starving, aspiring Country music man with a pregnant wife and a three-year-old daughter. I probably should have stayed in the Marine

Corps and gone for "the twenty." Hell, I was a Sergeant when I was only twenty-one! Now, here I was, twenty-three with a busted fuel pump on my brand new 1959 Ford and standing on the side of Highway 190 deep in Louisiana forty-five miles from Baton Rouge, hitchhiking a ride in the dark.

The wool suit was beginning to scratch my legs, as I tried to reconstruct the last three months of my life in my mind. My wool pants were also beginning to make my crotch itch, as I shifted from one foot to the other, trying to stay warm.

Damnit, to hell! I'm going to the mansion tonight. I ain't giving up, I thought. After all, the Governor said to come. Damn, here comes a car from the opposite direction. Looks like he's doing eighty-five miles per hour. Sure wish he'd turn around, I thought. As the car swooshed by, I saw the brake lights grow brighter. I'll be damn, he's slowing down. . . well shit fire and save matches, the son-of-a-gun is turning around. . . ain't that a lick! I thought. As the old '49 Ford started coming back toward me, I could see the small silver bullet-shaped nose loom larger on the front end between the two glaring headlights. As it got closer, I could see the sandpaper marks over the streaks of rust on the hood and fenders. It had been stripped of all of the original paint, waiting for a new coat. The four occupants inside were in their late teens or early twenties, I surmised.

"Hey, Buddy, you want a lift?" the whiskey-laden voice of the driver exclaimed loudly.

"Yea, you gonna get your ass wet," one of the passengers cried out drunkenly.

"He's a pretty boy with that suit and tie on, ain't he," came the cry from the back seat.

"You play that guitar?" the driver asked, as I climbed into the back seat with the other two passengers.

"Some," I replied, thinking to myself, that I had jumped from the frying pan into the fire. These guys were drunk and dangerous.

"Where you going?" the driver shouted toward the back seat with a half-turned head.

"To the Governor's mansion," I shot back as dignified as I could in a wet suit with a plastered head of hair.

"To the Governor's mansion?" he smirked. "Yea Buddy, that's where we gonna take you. . . to the Governor's mansion alright," he sneered. "By the way, what's the address?" he jeered.

"Yea, what's the address, Cinderella," the other chimed in.

"It's on North Boulevard," I replied calmly.

My insides were churning. Their whiskey breaths were making me nauseous. I knew I was in a precarious position speeding down the Highway at eighty miles an hour in a wreck just looking for a place to happen.

"Who are you anyway, big shot?" the passenger in the right front seat questioned.

"I'm Jay Chevalier. I wrote and recorded 'The Ballad of Earl K. Long' and you better get me to the mansion in one piece or Governor Long is gonna be mad as hell," I blurted out.

The car slowed automatically. I felt a sobering effect go through the occupants of the old Ford. That was the first time I had felt the power of Earl K. Long's name. Even to a drunken mind and at a distance far removed from the mansion, it carried authority and respect. The tone of the conversation changed as someone said, "You the same Jay Chevalier we heard singin' on the radio?"

"Yep," I said, as I reached for a record inside my guitar case, which was pinned between my legs, with the neck under my chin.

"Prove it," another voice said.

"Here. . . Here's the record with my name on it," I said. They grabbed the multicolored record label and passed it around and on to the driver.

"I'll be a son-of-a-bitch," he said. "We got us a real, live celebrity." He pressed the accelerator down, and we headed for Baton Rouge and those tall white columns on the mansion.

The old Ford pulled up into the circular driveway of the Governor's mansion and dropped me off. "Thanks fellas," I said to my now-sober young companions.

"Good luck, Jay. . . We'll be listening for you," they said, almost in unison, as they left me standing alone in front.

It was nine p.m. I turned to see their brake lights brighten just for an instance, as they slowed to turn onto North Boulevard, and then fade quickly out of sight and into the dark. I would never see them again, but I was grateful for the ride as I turned back to face the biggest and most imposing double front doors I had ever seen in my life.

It had quit raining. I hitched up my pants, picked up my guitar, suitcase, amplifier and courage to walk up the steps to those big old doors. I wondered, what next? as I punched the doorbell button with all the force that my new found courage could muster. The chimes seemed to ring forever inside the mansion, as they faintly drifted outside to my ears. No one answered. Maybe they are all at the ballgame, I speculated in my mind. After all, it's Saturday. . . I can't expect anyone to be home, I thought. I punched the button again. Just as I started to sit down on my up-turned suitcase in despair, the door creaked open very slowly.

"Yes," the voice was long, steady, southern and drawn out. I snapped to attention as I looked into the eyes of Lt. Simmons, the State Trooper in charge of the mansion this evening. He was very well-groomed, with shiny shoes and razor-sharp military creases in his freshly pressed State Trooper's uniform. He had a no-nonsense appearance as he stood there with a big pistol strapped on his side.

"My name is Jay Chevalier. . . I wrote and recorded 'The Ballad of Earl K. Long', the Governor invited me to go to the football game with him and to spend the night here in the mansion," I stammered. "My car broke down and I had to hitchhike a ride," I went on. "Here's my two tickets to the game," I added as I pulled them out from the coat pocket to display as further proof of my authenticity.

"Would you repeat that and just a little slower," he requested sternly. I repeated my statement this time slower and in my most convincing salesman-like manner. "Just a moment," he said as he closed the door in my face.

It seemed like an eternity before the door opened again. When it did Lt. Simmons cheerfully said, "Come in, Mr. Chevalier." I stepped into the warm brightly lit foyer. "If you'll follow me, I'll show you to your room. . . It is right down this hallway," he added. Lt. Simmons had talked to Sgt. Butler on the two-way radio and Governor Long had instructed them in no uncertain terms to take good care of me.

I didn't know it at the time, but this was to become my permanent room as long as the Governor was in office. The hot shower and clean bed sheets felt good. As I slipped between the covers of my new bed, I wondered at the strange turn of events. It seemed like the best things always happened to me when it rained. I drifted into a peaceful sleep, wondering what tomorrow would bring.

Chapter 2

"Hired"

It's one thing to be hired for a job you desire and another to get the pay you think you deserve.

Negotiating both with the most famous Governor Louisiana has ever known proved to be a lesson in good old fashioned Southern horse trading. The Governor was an expert and I was a fast-learning novice.

The art of this deal would bring together an aging political race horse and a young musical stud for the ride of a lifetime. The Governor was running to survive and I was running to arrive!

It was a two-lane blacktopped road we were traveling on, headed for the End of the World Bar. I was to learn later that the road just followed the bayou and stopped . . . stopped dead-end at a huge Cajun nightclub and bar. I wondered whether Huey or Earl had built such a good road as we sped along to our first two speaking engagements at Bayou Sorrell and Bayou Pigeon.

Earlier this morning, I had awakened in the mansion to the smell of bacon and eggs frying in the kitchen. As the fresh smell of south Louisiana dark-roast coffee wafted through the mansion and into my bedroom, I dreamily tried to reconstruct and make sense of the events the night before. After a hearty breakfast with the Governor and some of his cronies, we left hurriedly for the bayou country speakings. The Governor planned all of his Sunday stump speakings to be held in Cajun country. He said, "Cajuns love music, politics, whiskey and spicy foods any day of the week and most especially on Sunday." Because they were Catholic, after mass and confession, Sunday was wide open in Cajun country. It was not that way in predominantly Baptist north Louisiana. Therefore, Sunday politicking and events were always reserved for south Louisiana.

The Governor loved the Cajun people (although he couldn't speak a word of French), and they loved him. They knew that their way out of the swamps had been made easier because of the paved roads Huey and Earl had built in their earlier administrations. Although Uncle Earl, as they fondly called him, had just come out of two mental institutions, they were still going to vote for him. After all, hadn't they been run out of their homeland in Nova Scotia to be resettled strangers in a foreign land? Forty-five hundred Cajun refugees had made their way to south Louisiana, homeless, destitute, hungry and helpless, except for an indomitable spirit and courage that would carve out a new Garden of Eden for a future 2.5 million descendants. When they were relegated to the swamps of Louisiana, no one knew then, least of all the powers to be, that under those swamps flowed some of the richest oil veins in all of North America.

"Uncle Earl was crazy all right, crazy like a fox," the Cajuns liked to say. They had gathered around the old pickup truck as I started tuning my guitar, drawn by the magic of the moment. They loved music! Guitars, fiddles and accordions would set a Cajun's blood to rushing and his toes a-tapping like a young bridegroom's heart a-fluttering on his wedding night. Somewhere coursing through my Creole French blood, I felt an empathy for and a oneness with these fiery blooded bayou Frenchmen. "Ayee," someone shouted as I sang "Big Mamou," "Jolie Blonde," and "The Ballad of Earl K. Long." That exciting Cajun yell, different from the hillbilly hollering of the mountain folk, or the twang of a cowboy's yodel, could spur a young singer on to new heights never known before. Yes sir, this Sunday morning, I fell in love with bayou politicking and the Cajun people. Thanks to Uncle Earl and the Catholic Cajun people, Sundays would never be the same again!

The Governor made the two speakings without incident. Reciting time and again how the Longs had paved the way and roads for their bayou younguns to get an education; how the free school books, free hot lunches and the old age pension were the brain child of old Uncle Earl himself. Even though he was Baptist, Long told the Cajuns that the good Catholic people of Loyola University of New Orleans, helped him become a lawyer and what he was today he owed a great deal to those good Catholic teachers.

After giving out free bags of groceries at both speakings, we were finally heading back toward Baton Rouge. I sat deep in thought in the back seat of the big black Oldsmobile, as Sgt. Butler deftly guided us through the Cajun swamps with poke salad and palmetto growing alongside the roadway. The governor was quiet, half dozing in the right front seat.

Damn. . . a lot had happened in the last forty-eight hours, I marveled to myself. Just last Thursday night I had shown up on the steps of the courthouse in Bossier City in north Louisiana and brazenly walked up on the speaker's stand to sing "The Ballad of Earl K. Long," with no invitation from anyone! The Governor must have liked my brass because he invited me to attend a speaking with him the next night in Mansfield. It rained and we had to go inside the courthouse. I sang in front of the judge's bench in the courtroom for about fifty or sixty people. The Governor spoke as I sat in the jury box and listened. He then invited me to spend the night over at Frank and Ruth Mathews' camp. Frank and Ruth owned the King Lumber Company and were very wealthy. They were close friends of the Governor and I was invited to a party later that evening at their home.

I brought my guitar. Edgar Coco (a candidate for State Insurance Commissioner) had his harmonica. They rolled back the living room rug and danced to our music. While the whiskey flowed freely, the Governor gleefully held court in the corner of the room. He was seated in a big old easy chair with his toes tapping to every song. He truly enjoyed the music and loved to see the dancers twirl around the room. He chain-smoked Lucky Strike cigarettes and would call out a favorite selection every once in a while. As he sipped his Old Forester Bourbon and Coke, I knew this was the start of something big for the kid from Forest Hill, Louisiana. Finally, as the party wound down, the Governor invited me to make all five speakings the next day. Hell, that was just yesterday, I thought.

As I woke up Saturday morning, the sun was coming up over the forty-acre private lake outside of the Mathews' large camp house. About twelve of us had spent the night at the camp. Edgar Coco had gotten up, took his usual drink of whiskey from the ever present pint in his hip pocket and exclaimed, "It's gonna be a great day for politickin'." Edgar Coco was a Cajun Frenchman from Marksville, which is located in the northern part of Cajun Country. I already liked Edgar better than anyone else I had met around Uncle Earl. We were to become life-long friends. Today, he would unwittingly become my booking agent.

Edgar told me to follow him to the first political speaking of the day, down at the rural Flatwoods community. The sun was shining hot, bright, and directly into my eyes as I began to sing to the rather large crowd gathered around the old store front. They were dressed in khakis, bibbed overalls and blue jeans this Saturday morning in the piney wood hills of Flatwoods. I wondered why they called it Flatwoods as I squinted my eyes and caught the glint of sunlight on a red headed lady standing next to a trim-figured blonde at the edge of the crowd. I began to sing "The Ballad of Earl K. Long." The crowd started clapping along with the music and the two out-of-place female city slickers' toes started tapping in their spiked high-heeled shoes. Must be from out-of-town, I thought. Maybe, they're Earl's girls, I mused.

"Give Jay a hand. . . That's a great song about Old Uncle Earl," Edgar Coco said as he stepped up to the microphone and began to give his speech about the office he was running for. I stepped down off the porch thinking how much I liked the sound of applause. It gave me a tingling sensation much like a small, warm, electric current running through my body. It felt a little like the sex urge that would sometimes pop up spontaneously in my young, muscular frame.

"So, you're Jay Chevalier," the redhead said coyly but matter-of-factly.

"Yep. . . who are you?" I replied, as I glanced over at the blonde.

"Irma Tucker," she shot back, as her large bust kinda stuck out, like they'd just been inflated with pride.

"You work for the Governor?" I queried.

"Right. We're from Baton Rouge and this is Nancy Gibbs," she stated emphatically.

"Morning, Miss Gibbs," I mumbled. "You work for the Governor, too?" I went on.

"You bet. Today we'll pass out some fliers, listen to what the folks have to say, help get the crowd worked up with applause, and report back to Uncle Earl later," she stated rather calmly.

"You working for the Governor, Jay?" Irma chimed in.

"Well, uh, no, not really, you see, I'm just donating my time today, kinda just helpin' out," I stammered.

"Well you oughta be full-time. These people like music, and besides, they need something to pep up these rallies. After all, they're running against Jimmie Davis, and he's got a big band, plus a gospel quartet, and Moon Mulligan on the piano," Irma huffed indignantly as she swirled a clear looking liquid around in her paper cup. "We need to put a bug in his ear, Nancy," Irma winked. "See ya at the next stop, Jay." Irma shouted over her shoulder as both overly-dressed women wiggled their way through the crowd.

Edgar was red-faced and out of breath as he shook hands, working the crowd coming toward me. "You ready to go on to the next speaking?" he intoned breathlessly.

"You bet," I replied. "By the way, you sho' play a mean harp on 'Jambalaya'. You want me to back you up on the guitar at the next speaking?" I praised him generously.

"Damn right. That'd be great. I'm gonna see if Earl won't hire you full time," Edgar said, as his chest swelled with pride from my compliment about his harmonica playing. "Besides, we need music. It makes the people excited and livens up the crowd. How much you want to go to work full-time?" Edgar questioned with a bourbon twinkle in his flashy Cajun eyes.

"Hell, I don't know, Edgar. See if he'll go for $500 a week and all my expenses," I stated as seriously as I could for a fellow out of work and broke.

"Five hundred dollars, huh? Well, I guess you would have to give up all of your bookings if you went with us full-time. I'll see what he says and let you know at the next place," Edgar said, as he unlocked the door on his car.

"Thanks," I replied, nodding in serious agreements about all of those bookings I didn't have to give up.

As I hopped into my car and quickly left the old General Store at Flatwoods, the Governor was just beginning his speech. Curt Siegelin had introduced him to roaring applause and "give 'em hell, Uncle Earl" shouts from the crowd. That electric, tingling sensation was sweeping over my body, as I headed for nearby Boyce and a date with destiny.

The crowd at high noon in Boyce was a repeat of Flatwoods. However, we were on the edge of the Red River bottom land farms, and the crowd had a certain rural sophistication that was different from the piney woods people. I stepped up on the back of the old pickup truck with the single microphone stand on the tailgate. I surveyed the crowd, as I strummed the strings of my guitar to check the tuning. Sure enough, there was Nancy and Irma, still somehow looking out of place, dressed to the nines in their high-heeled shoes, working this country gathering of people curious about Earl K. Long. As I broke into my routine, I saw Edgar furiously working the crowd with his coattail a-flapping in the breeze. I wondered had he talked to the Governor about me going to work full-time. As I started to sing "Kansas City," the crowd moved closer to the old pickup truck. Irma looked up, winked and threw a flirtatious, all-knowing smile my way. I really had the crowd swinging as I broke into "The Ballad of Earl K. Long." To my surprise, I said, "Ladies and gentlemen, I'd like to introduce you to the best damned Frenchman in Louisiana and your next State Insurance Commissioner, Edgar Coco from Marksville." Edgar's big barreled-chest ballooned with pride at the heartfelt introduction and I knew then we would be friends for a long time, as he gave the best speech of his political career. As his hands waved and flapped wildly in the air, I just hoped the pint of whiskey didn't fall out of his hip pocket in front of this mostly Baptist, red-necked crowd.

As Irma sidled up next to me, I could feel the sexual electricity snap from her fall wool skirt. The faint smell of vodka was on her breath as she whispered, "Edgar really liked that introduction. You're on the right track now. I told the Governor I liked the music today," she went on dropping a hint that I should be beholden to her as her large breasts brushed against my arm.

"What'd he say?" I said.

"Just winked and nodded. But that's a lot from Uncle Earl," she stated.

"Well, guess I'd better go. I'll see you and Nancy in Bunkie and thanks a lot, Irma." I said as I squeezed her hand goodbye.

Edgar Coco came off the pickup truck after he had introduced Curt Siegelin catching me just before I got into my car. "Did you talk to Uncle Earl about my job?" I asked.

"Sure did," he replied.

"Well, what did he say?" I asked anxiously.

"He said, 'Five hundred dollars! Who in the hell does he think he is, Elvis Presley?'" Edgar quoted gleefully.

"What does that mean, Edgar?" I asked.

"Means he's interested, but not at five hundred dollars."

"Well, tell him four hundred fifty and all my expenses," I quipped.

"Okay. See you in Bunkie. By the way, thanks for the introduction," Edgar grinned. "That was real professional," he went on.

It was hotter than hell at two p.m. in Bunkie. The fall sun had come out extra bright and hot. As the sweat began to drip from under my arm pits and run down inside my shirt, I wondered why I had chosen to wear a wool suit with coat and tie. We were on a large railroad depot platform and it made it harder to reach the large crowd that was gathering. Because we were about four feet off the ground, I could easily see the back of the crowd. Irma looked a little tipsy as she got out of her car across the street and strolled toward the platform. The sound trucks were blaring out music, working the back streets as the driver would periodically, over his microphone, invite people to the Earl K. Long speaking and political rally.

"With plenty of refreshments, free bags of groceries and good music. . .hear and see in person, Earl K. Long and his statewide ticket speak in person at two p.m. in downtown Bunkie," he blared out.

As if by magic, the Saturday afternoon crowd started to get larger, coming in from the side streets and back country roads. Some had dust on their hats and bandanas in their hip pockets as it was still harvest time in the full cotton fields. Only Earl K. Long could draw a crowd like this away from their busy fall harvest. After the speaking, the crowd would melt just as quickly back into the countryside.

Clutching their large paper cups, Irma and Nancy swung and swayed through the crowd coming toward the speaker's stand. I wondered, had she talked to Uncle Earl anymore, as I jumped down to the ground.

"Hi there, cutie," she purred. "I told Uncle Earl he'd better hire you before Jimmie Davis did," Irma said, nonchalantly flipping her red hair in the sunlight.

"What did he say," I replied anxiously.

"He said, 'You think so?' and kinda arched his eyebrows. He'll hire you, Jay, if you play your cards right and your price ain't too high," Irma went on.

"Well, I don't know," I replied. "I really appreciate what you're doing, Irma. Regardless of what happens, let's stay in touch. Write your address down and when I come to Baton Rouge, I'll look you up."

"Here's my phone number. Just call anytime, "she cuddled up closer and I could tell the vodka was warming places I better be careful of, although I felt Irma was sincere in wanting to help me. I wondered how I would repay her.

As I hopped back up on the speaker's platform, Edgar was just getting out of his car. I waited for Edgar to work his way through the crowd with great anticipation. I reached down to give him a hand up to the platform. "Did you tell the Governor what I said?" I asked quickly.

"Yep," he replied.

"Well, what did he say?" I asked anxiously.

"'Son of a bitch' was all he said" Edgar grinned.

"What's that mean?" I asked meekly.

"I guess you're still too high," Edgar shot back.

"Hell. Tell him three hundred fifty dollars," I said, lowering my price a whole hundred dollars. Edgar grinned.

"Okay. I think we got him on a roll. Besides, I told him tomorrow is when we'll need you, because we'll be in Cajun country and you know how those Cajuns love music!" I thanked Edgar and turned back to the task at hand.

It was three p.m. when I left Bunkie heading for nearby Melville. I hadn't talked to the Governor all day as I had to go ahead of everyone else. I made up my mind to talk with him in Melville as it was the last speaking and we'd all show up there.

The Governor seemed to wake up as if by magic as the Oldsmobile skillfully glided up to the ferry ramp at Port Allen for the crossing to Baton Rouge. He half-turned in his seat as his gruff voice boomed out with authority, startling me out of my back seat reverie of the past two days. "Tell ya what I'll do," he stated. "I'll pay you two hundred a week plus your expenses and give you a place to stay at the mansion for the duration of the campaign. How's that sound? he exclaimed persuasively.

"Fantastic," I cried, reaching to shake his outstretched hand from back across the seat. "You'll never regret it, Uncle Earl," I prophesied. "And thanks a lot," I went on. He turned around in his seat, satisfied with the deal he had just made, as the Oldsmobile pulled up on the ferry. I could hardly contain the excitement inside my soul as a warm, vibrant, feeling flooded throughout my body.

By God, I had a job, the thought reverberated through my mind. Not just any old job, either. I was working for the Governor of Louisiana. I had to tell someone, anyone, quick as I could, I thought to myself, or I'll burst. This was the best day of my life, I thought as the Oldsmobile pulled up to the front of the Governor's mansion. I had been hired. I was hired by the most powerful man in the State of Louisiana. My life would never be the same again. My ship was set on a dead-ahead, full throttle, damn the torpedoes course, with what seemed a predestined fate!

Chapter 3

"Mississippi Showdown"

There are never any winners in a talent contest. Behind the scenes politics spoils the outcome for the real winners who are somewhere back in the pack.

Never was this so evident as in the Jimmie Rodgers Country Music Festival Contest that I had entered in June, 1959. Broken hearts and broken dreams shattered like glass in the chaos of the struggle whose ending had been predetermined by the string pullers of Nashville.

But some of us like the fabled Phoenix rose to the top of our game within days, weeks and months of the dying applause in Meridian, Mississippi.

Jimmy Stretch leaned against the parking meter with one arm stretched over the top as he gestured with his free hand emphasizing the point he was making. I stood with my back against the old brick wall outside of the Ranch Inn Dance Hall and Lounge. As I placed my foot against the wall to help support my relaxed stance, I heard the sickening thud of flesh against flesh. In shocked disbelief, I saw Jimmy flying through the air landing in a kneeling position in the middle of the street. A huge blurring, shadowy figure had lumbered between us and headed for the door twenty feet away. Seconds before, Pee Wee had told Jimmy good night and was now opening the door to enter the Ranch Inn Lounge when this huge bulk of a man grabbed him from behind, lifted him off the ground in a deadly bear hug and shouted, "You! You're the one! You son-of-a-bitch!"

My reflex action was instantaneous as I took two steps forward to help Jimmy up off the pavement. I was transfixed in mid-stride as the big man shouted, "I'm gonna tear your head off!" Whirling in mid-stride, I bounded toward Pee Wee's assailant leaping high in the air. I landed with both knees in his back and proceeded to pull with all my might as I squeezed the hammer lock I had around his head and neck even tighter. He loosened his grip on Pee Wee and reached back over his head with both hands trying to grab a handful of my slicked-down greasy, Beryl-creamed duck-tailed Elvis pompadour. As he loosened his grip, Pee Wee elbowed him in the gut and we both fell to the pavement with me on him like a rodeo bull rider without spurs.

A crowd gathered around as I cinched my grip around his neck tighter, afraid to let go. My mind quickly estimated his weight to be about two hundred fifty pounds. To my surprise, he didn't move. As Mr. Herrington, the bar owner, stood over us both with a three-foot-long two-by-four hollering, "Let him up. . . Let him up. . . I'll knock his head clean off!" As I slowly loosened my grip, I realized Pee Wee had knocked the wind out of him with his elbow. As we fell to the ground face forward, he had actually passed out, probably from all the alcohol he had consumed earlier.

My legs were trembling as I slowly got up. Mr. Herrington's two-by-four was still raised high and ominously as the squad car pulled up with sirens blaring and red lights flashing. "What's going on here? Is he dead?" the Alexandria policeman asked rapidly.

"No sir. . . I think he's passed out," I replied.

"What caused all this?" the officer questioned.

"The son-of-a-bitch was trying to beat up on my band members. I want him arrested for disturbing the peace, being drunk, breaking up my paying crowd and whatever else you can think of. . . I'll be down later to file an official complaint," Mr. Herrington blurted out as the officer snapped the cuffs on this would-be trouble maker.

As the big man stood up and drunkly staggered to the patrol car, I realized how large and tall he was. Towering over the arresting officer, he meekly got into the patrol car. As they drove off, I turned my attention back to Jimmy Stretch, "Are you all right?" I asked.

"Yeah. . . I'm O.K. but he sho' cold-cocked me up side of the head." Jimmy exclaimed rubbing the left side of his head and face.

"Why'd he hit you?" I queried.

"Well, the best I can tell is he and some little guy got in an argument inside the club while you all were playing music. When you took your intermission, the little guy invited this big guy outside to settle their differences. They went around the corner there to Bolton Avenue. As they started to talk, the little fellow jumped straight up in the air, popped the big fellow in the nose, and took off running. He came around the corner, ran between us as we were talking and as Pee Wee was opening the door to go back into the club. When the big guy came around the corner and between us, he was so mad he just reached out and slung his arm backwards catching me upside the head with a glancing blow. But when he saw Pee Wee at the door, he mistook Pee Wee for the one that hit him. It's a good thing you jumped in the middle of his back cause he was madder than hell at that little fellow for poppin' him in the nose. I guess we were a victim of mistaken identity," Jimmy said.

"Well, I'm sorry this had to happen," I stated anxiously. Jimmy was one of the most important people in the record industry at this time. He was public relations man and the road record distributor for RCA Victor. The recording artists' records he handled included Chet Atkins, Jim Reeves, Eddie Arnold, Don Gibson, and of course, Elvis Presley. He called on record stores and radio stations in three states. More importantly, I had just asked him to become my personal manager and help guide me through the nationally-known Jimmie Rodgers Country Music Festival Contest coming up in Meridian, Mississippi in about thirty days. I wanted to be a nationally-known professional country music entertainer more than anything else in the world. My heart ached for the day that I could earn my living by just playing Country music. The driving, burning sensation inside me was like an all consuming fire of desire. Because of some stupid drunk hitting my future manager over the head outside a two bit honkytonk on Washington Street in Alexandria, in central Louisiana, my ambitions may never see the light of day, I worried in my mind.

"Don't worry about it, Jay" Jimmy replied. "Someday, we'll look back on this and laugh. It will be one of the stories we'll tell our grandchildren," he went on. "This was my first time to hear you and the whole band together. You all sounded great and the people loved you. Mr. Herrington said you were one of the best draws he's ever had at the Ranch Inn. He said all you need is a break and a record. I agree. Come by the house tomorrow. We'll discuss getting ready for Meridian and the contest," he stated as he saluted good night and started across the street to his car. In stunned silence, I watched Jimmy drive off savoring the few words he'd just said. This night that started off so bad was the beginning of a lifelong friendship. You never can tell how things are gonna work out, I thought as I stepped under the flashing neon sign and back into the hustle and bustle of Louisiana honky-tonk nightlife.

Wondering where the little guy went who had started the fight, I made my way through the dancers and to the bandstand while Hank Williams sang, "Hey Good Lookin'" on the juke box.

"You got a request for "In the Jail House Now" and "Cold Cold Heart" from that little dude sitting over in the corner," Pee Wee said as I stepped back upon the bandstand.

"Hell, I don't care. I'm going to Meridian, Mississippi next month. I'm gonna win that Jimmie Rodgers Country Music Festival contest if it's the last thing I do," I quickly replied to Pee Wee.

"Jimmy said he'd take you over, huh?" Pee Wee grinned.

"Yep, we're gonna be stars, partner. So get out your writing pen and let's write a hit," I laughingly shot back to my song-writing partner and best friend.

Sunday down south is a day of church-going, Saturday night recuperations, fried chicken dinner and Sunday afternoon visiting. I'd been to church, heard the preacher pray over all of us back-sliding sinners, and had eaten Mamma's fried chicken. Now I was ready to get down to some serious business with Jimmy Stretch. I parked my car in front of the white-framed house on Hill Street in Pineville, across the Red River from Alexandria. I opened the door to get out and felt the breeze of young Jerry Stretch's bicycle as he whizzed by. His younger sister, Patricia, was on the front porch with a pouty look on her face because her older brother wasn't giving her a ride on his disappearing bicycle down the long sidewalk. "Your daddy home?" I inquired.

"Yep, he's inside asleep on the couch and mama's washing the dishes," she shot back. "Watcha want?" she flipped her hair as I knocked on the door. "You selling something? They don't like salesmen," she went on as I continued to knock.

"Bill, would you get the door? I need to slip on a shirt," I heard Jimmy's voice from within. As the door opened, a strikingly slender, well-modulated voiced woman said, "You must be Jay Chevalier. Jimmy's expecting you. Come on in."

"You must be Mrs. Stretch" I hesitated.

"Yes, yes. Just call me Bill, everyone else does. Now come on in. Musicians are welcomed here," she stated matter-of-factly. I quickly stepped into the cozy living room as Jimmy greeted me buttoning up his loose fitting shirt.

"Have a seat, Jay," Jimmy said as he gestured to an overstuffed chair. I sank down into the cushion as Jimmy went on. "I'm getting ready to go on the road in a couple of hours. I'll be spending the night in Natchez and then work my way on to Meridian, Mississippi by Tuesday," he said as if everyone had a job this glamorous. "We're doing a special promotion this week on Jim Reeves' new record 'Billy Billy Bayou.' We're coat-tailing it in with Elvis' new release, therefore assuring Jim of a lot of airplay. When you piggyback a promotion like this, it really helps all the artists on the label, and airplay is the name of the game. It's the key to record sales and that's the bottom line," he stated with authority. "It feeds the family, and with two young ones to raise it keeps me hopping out on the road four to five days a week," he affirmed.

"Gosh, Jimmy, I knew what you did was important, but I didn't realize you stayed gone so long and that you were away from your family so much. How does Mrs. Stretch put up with that?" I questioned.

"That's Bill to you if you don't mind" she snapped briskly. "Besides Jimmy's home most of the weekends, and we do get to meet a lot of the recording stars, so it does have some extra rewards," she added.

"Yes, m'am, I guess so. Have you ever met Elvis or Chet Atkins?" I asked wide-eyed.

"Sure have, plus Eddy Arnold, Jim Reeves and Skeeter Davis," she quipped.

"I'd give my front seat in Hell to meet Chet," I blurted out. "Excuse me for using that word. It just slipped out. Sometimes, I think I'm still in the Marine Corps and I slip up with some of my old military adjectives," I apologized to Ms. Bill.

"Please call me Bill and don't worry about apologizing. If we took the word 'Hell' out of our vocabulary all the preachers would be out of business. I'm going to make us some coffee. You and Jimmy get on with your meeting. Jay, make yourself at home. I have a feeling we're going to be seeing a lot of you around here anyway. Jimmy seems to attract stray birddogs, cats and lonesome musicians. Who knows, you might fit in all three categories," she laughed as she headed for the kitchen. I shrugged and laughed too. Somehow, the name Bill didn't seem so odd after all. Little did I know how important Bill's future conversations and encouragements would be to this struggling guitar picker who would sometimes catch a nap on the Stretch's couch between classes at Louisiana College after having played half the night away in the local honky-tonks of central Louisiana.

"How much you know about the Jimmie Rodgers Country Music Festival contest?" Jimmy asked as he straightened out his road briefcase.

"Not much. Just that it's the most important country music contest in the nation and that Jimmie Rodgers started it all with his first recordings for RCA Victor back in the twenties, I guess," I replied while handing Jimmy some publicity pictures of Elvis and Jim Reeves for his trip to Mississippi.

"Well, you are right about that. He was the inspiration for Ernest Tubb, Hank Snow, Roy Acuff and Gene Autry, just to name a few of his protégés. Almost anyone who's in the business today got their start from listening to the old Jimmie Rodgers seventy-eight's playing on a wind-up Victrola," Jimmy stated with authority. "Mrs. Jimmie Rodgers is still living and will be there to help present the grand prizes. His daughter, Anita, is coming in from San Antonio and one of his aunts whom he collaborated with will be there. Ernest and Hank will be co-hosts, and will perform with their bands. They're expecting seven to eight thousand people on the final night. The finals will be held in Ray Football Stadium. It's the only place big enough to hold the crowd that's anticipated for the final night," Jimmy exclaimed.

My heart was racing and my pulse resounded in my mind like the thumping of the water pumps in the rice fields of south Louisiana. The adrenaline that flowed through my body as Jimmy talked stirred up the same excitement as a runaway grass fire in the piney wood hills, whipped into a destructive fiery frenzy by an unabated southwestern wind from east Texas.

"What's the rules? Who are the judges? What's your suggestion and when do we get started?" I barked like a U.S. Marine drill instructor forgetting Jimmy was right there as I bounded to my feet and into that Mississippi spotlight in my mind. I could hear the applause, see the crowd and feel the flush of winning first place.

When Jimmy said, "Hold on. Rome wasn't built in a day," it brought me back to reality.

"Yeah, but Caesar didn't have any Marines from Paris Island, South Carolina either," I quipped.

"That's a fact," Jimmy replied. "But it's going to take more than esprit de corps and hard charging to win this contest," he said. "However, it will take a lot of guts, a tremendous amount of planning, hard work, rehearsing, physical stamina and determination. What do you think?" he said.

"How much money?" I replied.

"What do you mean?" he raised an eyebrow.

"How much money you want to help me?" I stated.

"That's the least of my worries. I get paid whether you go to Meridian or not," he shot back. "I don't need any money, but you'll need some for expenses and whatever else you're going to do to promote yourself. You need to plan on being in Meridian for a week. You can stay with me so you don't have to worry about a room. I have reservations at the Lamar Hotel and a hospitality suite for disc jockeys and members of the press. It's paid for by RCA Victor and you can use the suite to campaign out of," he went on.

The coffee smelled good as Bill returned from the kitchen to join the conversation. "Why don't you just bring back all of the rules and regulations from your trip this week and then you two will know exactly what you're up against," Bill exclaimed.

"Good idea," Jimmy retorted, "and we can meet back here next Sunday, map out our game plan and get to work," he went on. Leave it to a woman to cut through all the bullshit, I thought. I knew then that I was going to like Bill and Jimmy Stretch for the rest of my life and I silently resolved to do something nice for the both of them some day. Maybe I'd buy Jimmy a new bird dog and Bill a new Cadillac.

The week dragged on and seemed to last forever. The college classes seemed boring compared to my thoughts and imaginations of winning the big Mississippi

Showdown Country Music Contest. I'd stopped by Jimmy's house a couple of times to see if Bill had heard from Jimmy about the contest rules. "He'll call Thursday night, he always does," she assured me. Sure enough, when I stopped by after class Friday afternoon Bill had heard from Jimmy.

"Be here Sunday afternoon around two p.m. He's bringing the rules back with him and the statistics on the number of contestants entering," she said.

"Thanks Bill. I'll see you Sunday. I've got to play music tonight and tomorrow night. Tell Jimmy to come by Saturday night if he can. I've got a new drummer I want him to hear," I stated anxiously. Bill nodded in agreement as I backed out the door heading for my new 1959 Ford.

The Ford was brand new. I'd spent my last few bucks for a down payment. I'd made up my mind to go to Meridian in style even if it cost me my last dollar. To be a winner, you got to look like a winner and a new blue and white 1959 Ford made me look like a winner even if it was only a six cylinder instead of a V-8. I'll bet Jimmy will be surprised. This will show him I'm dead serious about winning, I thought to myself as I pulled away from the curb and headed for Alexandria and the Ranch Inn Lounge.

Friday and Saturday night were uneventful except for me drinking too much Scotch and water. I'll never forget the first Scotch whiskey I ever drank. It was at the Fernwood Recording Studio in South Norfolk, Virginia. Norman Phelps who owned the studio told me, "Son, if you are gonna stay in the entertainment business, you're gonna be going to a lot of cocktail parties. If you want to look sophisticated whether in New York, Nashville or Hollywood, always order Scotch and water. It will make them think you are a man of the world. You see, everybody and his dog can't drink Scotch because it's so bad you have to acquire a taste for it." Norman stopped to let the effect of what he'd just said sink in. Then, he reached behind the portable bar in his office and withdrew a fifth of Cutty Sark. "Now, if you really want to show class, ask for Cutty and water. It's the very best Scotch there is. Here, have a shot," he went on. As I gulped down the whiskey from the green bottle with the yellow label, I wondered how in the world I would ever develop a taste for anything that tasted so bad. My face screwed up in a green-persimmon pucker so Norman laughed and said, "Don't worry, you'll learn to like it and you won't have any hangovers either."

Well, here I was four years later drinking Scotch with the best of the rednecks and pulpwood haulers of central Louisiana. When some high-rolling hillbilly wanted to buy a round of drinks, they'd always look kinda funny when I ordered Scotch and water. I never knew if it was my good taste or the high priced Cutty and water drink that impressed them.

While I never had a hangover from drinking Scotch, it damn sure wore me out and made me thirsty, I thought as I knocked on Jimmy's door this bright sunny Sunday afternoon. "Come in; the door's open," Bill said from within the house. As I stepped inside she said, "I knew it was you, Jay. You are always punctual and the clock inside just chimed two p.m. I guess the military kept you on time, huh?" she questioned.

"Yep, you are right as rain. I can't stand being late or having to hurry up and wait," I added. "Where's Jimmy?" I queried.

"In the kitchen," came Jimmy's reply. "I'm mixing us a drink. Do you want one?" he asked.

"No sir, just plain coke. After last night, I'm trying to quit," I joked.

"Tied one on did you?" he laughed as he came into the living room with the ice-cold refreshments. "Not really. I just tried to drink all of those free ones some high roller was buying for the band. I guess he was trying to impress some girl by getting close to the band. That's usually the case," I bragged. "Besides, the more money that goes in the till, the better the owner likes it," I philosophized.

"You ready to get serious about Meridian and the contest?" Jimmy asked with a concerned look on his face.

"I'd better be serious. I just spent all my money on a serious looking ride just so I'd look impressive in Mississippi," I shot back. "Come see, Jimmy," I urged.

"Whew boy, she's pretty. You'll have to fight those Mississippi girls off with a stick in that thing!" Jimmy exclaimed.

"Do you really like it?" I asked breathlessly.

"You bet," was the quiet reply. "You need to be different. Anything you can do to draw attention to yourself will help," Jimmy said. "Let's go inside and map out a plan."

The city lights of Meridian drew closer as my new Ford cut through the Mississippi twilight with the silent gracefulness of a towed glider plane that has just been cut loose at a ten-thousand-foot altitude carried by the hushed wind currents towards its predetermined destination. The Red Hot Restaurant and Truck Stop sign blared its blood-red neon welcome to the "CAJUN SENSATION" who was about to invade this historic Mecca of Country music.

The elevator seemed to move slowly going up to the fourth floor of the Lamar Hotel. I had called Jimmy from the house phone and he said to come on up. Wonder what you do on a Sunday night in Meridian? Not much, I speculated, as the elevator doors swung open by unseen mechanical hands. It always amazed me how you could punch one little button and send an electrical impulse to some hidden metal mind force that directed the elevator to start, stop, and open the doors on the correct floor of a hotel or tall office building. As I walked down the hall to Jimmy's room, I noticed a sign on the opposite door that read, "Hospitality Suite." That Jimmy is sure on the ball, I thought. As the hotel door responded to my shave-and-a-haircut-two-bits rhythmic tic-toc-tap. The light flooded into the hallway with Jimmy's enthusiastic greeting, "Come on in, the water's fine. How was your trip?"

"Howdy-do Mr. Stretch! It was fine. I see RCA has landed and you have everything under control," I bowed at the waist and gestured toward the hospitality suite.

"That's right. Bootlegged whiskey and all," he smiled.

"Bootlegged?" I quizzed.

"Yep. Mississippi's dry, but I have a friend on the police force who has a friend who is a friend of a bootlegger who supplied most of the whiskey," he said. Stepping around the cases of Kentucky bourbon and familiar Canadian Club labels, Jimmy said with glee, "I keep half the whiskey here in my room and the other half over in the hospitality suite across the hall. We'll only have the suite open a couple of hours each night starting Tuesday. Would you like to see it?" he went on.

"Sure would," I replied.

As Jimmy put the key in the door to open this special party room he said, "You'll meet a lot of important people here in the recording and entertainment business. You can sort of act as an unofficial co-host. Just remember – you are promoting RCA Record artists and their new releases," Jimmy said as he stepped over to the brightly lit juke box that was loaded down with all of the new RCA hits. "Just press the buttons. All of the plays are free. You can help keep the music flowing. We'll have a bartender each night and some hors d'oeuvres," Jimmy informed as I surveyed the immaculate white table cloths and sparkling cocktail glasses all stacked neatly in rows like spit-and-polish soldiers ready to be reviewed by the generals of the Country music industry. In our case, it would be D.J.'s, Nashville stars, dignitaries and the city officials from Meridian. So this was what Norman had been talking about when he had said four years ago, always order Scotch and water. Well, it wasn't New York, Nashville or Hollywood, but I sensed for me it was just as important, and best of all, I didn't have to pay for it.

"It's great, Jimmy. You can count on me to help," I exclaimed.

"Fine. Let's go get something to eat and go over our game plan," Jimmy said looking every bit the manager and man in control.

The Davis Grill was an all-night downtown café. "These folks are open twenty-four hours," Jimmy said as we stepped inside and headed for the big round table to our left. "You can meet everybody who is anybody here in Meridian," Jimmy said as we sat down at a big empty round table. "Matter of fact, this table is known as the Knights of the Round Table meeting place," Jimmy laughed seriously. "The movers and shakers meet here," he went on.

"What'll you have?" the waitress questioned. She seemed to appear out of nowhere with pad in hand.

"Black coffee and a hot roast beef sandwich," Jimmy shot back.

"How about you, cowboy?" she said as she sized me up and down, from my western-cut shirt to my flashy cowboy boots.

"Ditto," I replied as I flipped the ashes off my half-smoked cigarette.

"Ditto, ain't on the menu," she flirted.

"All right, you," I grinned.

"I ain't on the menu either. You guys in town for the Jimmy Rodgers Festival?" she queried.

"We sure are. I'm in the preliminary contest Tuesday night. You're coming?" I pressed for an answer.

"Nope. I don't like Country music. I like Rock 'n Roll, Fats Domino, Little Richard and Elvis," she replied matter-of-factly, "and I'm bringing you a hot roast beef just like your partner," she shot back over her shoulder as she headed for the kitchen.

"Uppity little split tail, ain't she?" I looked to Jimmy for confirmation.

"Yup. But I'm afraid if something's not done soon Rock 'n Roll is going to push Country music out the door" Jimmy said with a worried look on his face. "It's already out-selling Country records four-to-one. The economics will dictate which way the record business will go. I'm afraid if they don't find some new blood in the Country field, it'll be a thing of the past. That's why this festival is so important," Jimmy mused, turning the cup of hot coffee in small circles on the table, seeming to look for an answer in the hot black brew.

"Don't worry, Jimmy. The Grand Ole Opry and Nashville will never die. As long as there's lonesomeness in this old world and long-legged guitar pickers in honky-tonks, Country music will never die," I encouraged emphatically.

"I hope you are right," he said. "Now, let's get down to the plans for this week," he concluded.

"There were three hundred and fifty contestants nationwide who had sent in tapes. The judges have narrowed it down to approximately seventy-five performing finalists. There will be three winners picked each night from groups of fifteen to twenty. The preliminary contest will be held in different locations all over town with the twelve semi-finalists rounding it off to the top three on Friday night. These three finalists will then appear with the Ernest Tubb band on the big country music spectacular show Saturday night at Ray Football Stadium. Our job now is to get you into the top twelve and then into the top three. You have been officially entered and accepted. By the way, the VFW sponsorship from Alexandria was quite impressive," Jimmy stated.

"Well, you said I needed a non-profit organization, and my daddy's a member, plus I am a veteran even if I'm only twenty-three years old," I stated with pride. "Besides, they printed over two thousand publicity pictures of me with compliments of the Veterans of Foreign Wars on the bottom. I'm going to give one to everyone I meet. By the time we get to Saturday night, every contest audience member this week will know who I am. After my contest Tuesday night, I'll make all of the other shows, observe my competition and give everyone a free picture, especially all the older women and single girls. This way they'll applaud for the Cajun Sensation from Louisiana," I reasoned to Jimmy. "Plus, I've made a huge three-by-five foot plywood sign that fits like a triangle on top of my car that says in red, white and blue letters

'Jay Chevalier, The Cajun Sensation, Alexandria, Louisiana.' If it works for those politicians back home, it ought to work for us," I quipped to Jimmy who had gulped half of his coffee mesmerized by this piney woods upstart he had verbally agreed to help manage to a winning position.

"That's fantastic," Jimmy said. "Even though there'll be judges for each contest, I'm sure some of them will be swayed by the applause. Plus, the Thursday night contest is supposed to be judged by the most applause for the winner. We need to get you on the Earl Aycock, Jim Dowdy and Claude Gray D.J. shows over at WMOX Radio. They should give you good interviews since you are from out of town and with me. They'll hope I'll bring Jim Reeves, Hank Snow or Skeeter Davis by later," Jimmy stated with a confidence that only success and experience breeds.

Heads snapped on every corner in downtown Meridian trying to read the gaudy sign on top of the new blue and white Ford slowly cruising the sun-drenched streets. Every once in awhile, the driver would stop and give out leaflets at a busy intersection causing red-faced city policemen to blow their traffic whistles with the frantic vigor and waving arms of the keystone cops. Through the blare of car horns, the young country bumpkin moved seemingly oblivious to the commotion the free pictures and his free-wheeling, hand-shaking style of Louisiana political public relations were causing. This one-man parade was reminiscent of Senator Dudley J. LeBlanc and his forty car train celebrity Hadacol Caravan of the late 1940s. Though smaller in scope, to the young country music zealot from central Louisiana it was just as important.

"Whut's all the commotion about outside?" Earl Aycock quizzed his fellow Knights of the Round Table.

"Oh, Governor Jimmie Davis just arrived from Louisiana. He and Chris Fraser are checking in over at the Lamar. You know he's running for Governor of Louisiana again," Jim Dowdy said.

"Nope. I saw the Governor. I'm talking about that idiot with the sign on top of his car tying up all the traffic," Earl said impatiently.

"You mean the Cajun Sensation. That's Jimmy Stretch's new protégé. He's come over here to win the big contest. Hell, I can't even pronounce his name, Cavalier, Shavelier, Maurice or something like that."

The judges will have fun with that one, that's for sure," Claude Gray spoke up with booming authority in his voice.

"He'll never make it with a name like that. Hell, it don't even sound Country," someone else said.

"Don't be so sure. He's got lots of guts and Jimmy Stretch," Lee Roberts piped up from over in the corner. "Besides, I've met him and even though he's cocky as hell, women like his good looks. Whether he can sing or not makes no difference. Women buy records, concert tickets and concessions. If there are any women judges, he's got a hell of a chance. Who do you think made Elvis? Certainly, not the Knights of this Round Table," he grinned.

Jimmy was standing outside of the door of the Davis Café at noon just as he said he would be. As we shook hands, he introduced me to Carl Fitzgerald, one of the best D.J.'s in the South. "Pleased to meet you Mr. Fitzgerald," I stammered, shifting the stack of publicity pictures under my left arm.

"Carl, to you Jay," he said making me feel at ease instantly with that Mississippi radio voice. "Let's go in and I'll introduce you to the Round Table gang. You'll need their help and support. So give 'em your best shot," Carl said. Minutes later after all of the shaking and howdying, I seemed to fit in, thanks to Jimmy and Carl making a joke out of my name. It seemed to break the ice as they learned how to pronounce my name and then jokingly asked, was it true that a Cajun from Louisiana would eat anything?

"Yep, frog legs, crawfish, squirrel, gumbo, dirty rice and fried alligator tails," I allowed as I side-stepped the sexual insinuation from these Mississippi rednecks. Since I seemed to be one of the good old boys and harmless, I received several invitations for radio interviews. Jimmy and Carl had done a good job of fronting me in with the powers that be. I was grateful to Lee Roberts for offering to introduce me around town. This Monday was getting off to a great start, I thought as I finished eating my club sandwich and potato chips.

It was Tuesday and the night's excitement seemed to appear in my life as if by magic. The backstage area was crowded with contestants and the sound of twanging guitars being tuned. An electric tension permeated the air, as only the anticipation of would-be stars could generate. The contestant's minds, filled with sugar plum impressions of the Ted Mack Amateur Hour in New York and the Grand Ole Opry in Nashville, hurled telepathic messages back and forth across the room like lightning bolts in a west Texas thunderstorm. Cascading from corner to corner, this mental electricity charged the entire hall's audience, amplified by the thoughts of each contestant's own entourage of Mamas, Daddys, aunts, uncles, cousins, and other prejudiced peer groups. I stood alone backstage in the eye of the proverbial storm wondering how I was going to overcome the applause from the salted sections of the audience for my fellow contestants.

I had wrangled my way into being last on the roster of contestants. Somehow, I had theorized, that would be the best place to be as people and judges tend to remember what they see and hear last.

I had guessed right, for now I was receiving enough applause from all over the audience to assure me of a spot in the top three, I thought as I swung into the second of the two songs that were allowed each contestant. The spotlight felt good on my face as I bore down on the Jim Reeves RCA Victor record hit 'Billy Billy Bayou.'

Though blinded by the spotlight, I could feel toes tapping and the audience swaying to this rhythmical Louisiana story-song written by Roger Miller. I guess, since I had been introduced from out of town and the emcee sort of stumbled over my name, I seemed less threatening to the hometown favorite bands. To my surprise, the audience burst into loud applause as I bowed and stepped behind the back stage curtain to await the final verdict.

Moments later and after what seemed like an eternity, the emcee called my name out as one of the top three winners that night. My knees trembled and my face flushed as I ran out to take a bow with the other two, as the crowd pressed forward to get closer to this magical triage of winners. I reached for my ever-ready pictures, began shaking hands and signing autographs, and implored everyone to come and support me in the semi-finals Thursday night.

She was five-foot-two, had red hair, freckles, green eyes, a million dollar figure and could play the piano. Her daddy was a Methodist preacher and an insurance salesman, and she had a ten-year-old sister in the contest the next night who sang like Brenda Lee.

As I snapped my guitar case shut, she said, "You know you could win this contest if you had a local following like everyone else!"

Drawn by her straight forwardness, and the freckles peeping out from under her low cut dress that outlined her upturned breasts, I questioned, "Who are you?" in my best John Wayne western drawl.

"Precious Smith, and my family's kin to almost everyone in town," she purred through pouted lips.

"Who're you supporting in the contest," I asked.

"My ten-year-old sister, Peggy, and you," she shot back.

"Why me?" I questioned.

"Well, Peggy's only ten and they're really looking for someone who can go on to represent Meridian professionally nationwide.

"Besides, I like the way your jeans fit, and that black shirt with the white fringe turns me on," she stated honestly. "Anything wrong with that?" she went on.

"Nope. You want to go with me over to RCA's hospitality suite at the Lamar," I asked brazenly.

"Why not. Maybe we'll see Jim Reeves. You know you kinda look like Jim," she let the thought escape from her well-rounded lips.

Jimmy was right. Everyone who was anyone was in the hospitality suite. Precious seemed to know everyone there and she sure made our entrance look good, as Jimmy started introducing me around to the dignitaries of Meridian and Nashville. Precious was a one-woman PR firm as she told everyone how I won the contest. Several RCA executives noticed the women that swooned in the audience when I sang Jim Reeves'

"Billy Billy Bayou." Nat Vincent from Peer International in New York came over to give me his business card and said he was one of the judges that night. He asked if I was a songwriter and I said, yes. "You do know that Peer International is the publishing company that published all of Jimmie Rodgers's songs, don't you?" he questioned.

"No sir, but I sure do now and I won't ever forget it or meeting you. Is it all right if I send you some songs when I get back to Louisiana?" I said meekly.

"You bet. The hit song is the most important thing in the record industry. Without a hit song, there can be no recording stars. It all starts with the writer, my boy. Don't ever forget that," he emphatically said and punctuated his statement with the stirrer stick of his Cutty Sark and water.

It was getting late as Precious and I slipped between the clean crisp sheets of the bed in my room down the hall away from the dwindling noise of the hospitality suite. We'd told Jimmy we were going out to the Red Hot Cafe on the edge of town and then I'd take Precious home. Somehow, the warm feeling of the Scotch had sidetracked us on the way to the elevator. I'll be damn, she's redheaded all the way down, I thought as she turned over and into my arms to seal the deal we'd just made. She'd agreed to handle my publicity for the rest of the contest.

The cold cuts lining the long white table on this early Wednesday evening at Brother Smith's house looked ever so inviting. As the Reverend thanked God for the bounty on this table and the good health his family enjoyed, I wondered at the truly marvelous turn of events. He went on to ask God to protect and guide us all. To give his daughter and their honored guest success in the forthcoming great music contest was a most humbling request added by the Reverend just before his hearty amen!

Precious squeezed my hand she'd been holding throughout the prayer and said, "Dive in! You're gonna need all the strength you can get to keep up with me for the next few days."

Her mother nodded approvingly at the invitation to eat, as her daddy, with a plate full, announced that we'd have Peggy sing for us and Precious play the piano after our light meal. Peggy only nibbled at her food saying she couldn't sing on a full stomach. I knew how she felt as I wolfed down the cold cuts, pickles, carrots, radishes, sweet pickles and potato salad. I was glad I didn't have to sing in the contest tonight.

"You'll do great, Peggy," I encouraged, "besides, we'll start the applause for you and it'll just snowball from there," I prophesied, not knowing my prediction would come true just four hours later.

"How'd you know Peggy was going to win?" Precious questioned while slipping the turtle-necked blouse over her head and neatly placing it on the chair at the foot of my hotel room bed.

"Hell, I'm a prophet, soothsayer, and a connoisseur of good talent, singing or otherwise," I replied, confident in my ability to satisfy this Mississippi bomb shell.

"Well, you've certainly won Mom and Dad over with your Southern manners and the way you supported and encouraged Peggy," she agreed with an upturned smile.

"What about the older sister? What do you think? I asked cockily.

"You've still got a long way to go before Thursday and right now I wouldn't bet on the outcome one way or the other," she mused. "This is a funny town. You can be winning and still lose. You know what I mean?" she snapped.

"Nope. All I know is you smell good and I've always taken care of one thing at a time. What do you think about that?" I shot back.

"Well, Rhett, after all, tomorrow is another day," she said flamboyantly, gestured for emphasis and then flipped the light switch. The rustle of her falling poodle skirt filled the room. She silently made her way across the room. Her body silhouetted against the flashing neon light streaming through the open window. Precious was all woman! A Mississippi fireball in bed and sweet as a magnolia blossom in public. Her night time energy was unsurpassed and she carried on until the daylight hours.

Wednesday and Thursday, we made all the hot spots in town. Heard the rumors that a sixteen-year-old piano player by the name of Jimmy Elledge was a shoo-in to win. The Burt sisters were going to be a hard act to beat was a known fact. In all of that scuttlebutt around town, there was never any mention of a Ken Mabry. Some feedback said the kid from Louisiana had a chance even if it was a long shot. All the while, I kept signing autographs, giving out free pictures and shaking the hands of every woman, little girl or young ladies I could find. Even grandmas, grandpas and pulp wood haulers were not exempt from my relentless pursuit, trying to establish a base of support in Mississippi. Precious urged, cajoled, and called in favors from disc jockeys, business owners and anyone who would listen to get them to come to the contest Thursday to support me.

When Thursday rolled around, I was as keyed-up as a freshly wound eight-day clock. The seven judges were rumored to be Ernest Tubb, Hank Snow, Ted Mack, Chet Atkins, Harry Stone, Mack Wiseman, and Owen Bradley. If the rumor was true, this was a stellar panel and could make or break a young artist's career. At the end of the evening when the trophy was placed in my hand for being one of the top three finalists, I was beside myself with excitement. When we got back to the Lamar Hotel, Jimmy and I called home to alert my wife, parents and next of kin. Since there was no phone where I lived, the message had to be delivered and would prove heart-breaking later. "I guess we better go across the hall to the hospitality suite," Jimmy said.

"You go ahead. I'm going to change clothes. I really sweated this one out and I smell like it. I'll take a quick shower and be right over," I explained. I really wanted to savor the moment of winning a little more in my mind before going into the crowd of well-wishers at this evening's cocktail party.

The cold shower felt good after the hot water had opened the pores of my summer-tanned skin. The stinging icy drops of water against my face reminded me of the shockingly cold swift waters of Spring Creek back home at the old Shady Nook swimming hole. As the water ran down my stomach and between my young muscular legs, I wondered why I hadn't seen Precious at the end of the contest. I had looked everywhere for her in the crowd. Now, I just assumed she was across the hall probably talking to Jim Reeves or some other star. I'd better hurry I thought or somebody'll be beating my time. Besides, I wanted to know what she thought about my chances for winning first place Saturday night.

"Congratulations, Jay. We heard you did real well tonight," someone said as I walked into the RCA party suite. "Thanks. Have you seen Precious?" I asked the bartender.

"She's over in the corner," he nodded and pointed to the back of the room. One look and I knew something was wrong. Her eyes were red from crying, too much whiskey, or both, I thought.

"What are you doing in the corner Lil' Miss Muffett?" I said jokingly.

"Trying to get some courage and whey? Is that the right answer?" she snapped. I was shocked at her testiness.

"Nope, but it'll do," I still joked, not catching the drift of her mood.

"You hot blooded Frenchman, come over here, bed down a Mississippi rose, slide on back to Louisiana to your wives and girlfriends and think everything is just hunkydory, don't you?" she sobbed half-spilling her drink as her hands trembled in anger.

"What are you talking about?" I stammered.

"You know damn well what I'm talking about!" she half-shouted.

"Don't make a scene here, Precious. Let's go out in the hall and talk. You've had too much to drink," I whispered hoarsely guiding her by the arm through the crowd and out into the dimly lit hallway and beyond the din of the crowd. "Now, what's this all about?" I said propping her up against the wall for support.

"Damn it, why didn't you tell me you were married?" she gasped as hot tears fell from her cheeks and onto the back of my hand supporting her chin.

"You never asked me and besides who told you?" I snapped, angry at some invisible foe.

"Jimmy did tonight at the contest. We were standing at the back of the auditorium and I don't know why I asked him, but I just did. He said you were happily married and had a little girl too! I should have known better than to have fallen in love with you. All you damn musicians are just alike. You think the world owes you a living and every girl owes you a roll in the hay. Well, now you can go on back and brag to all your picking buddies you've had a roll with a Mississippi preacher's daughter. Big deal! You're not the first. You're just the only one I've cared about. So cheers! Here's to your fame and fortune. I hope you lose the contest to that sorry-ass Ken Mabry and I hope I never see you again," she screamed throwing the glass of bourbon in my face and running for the elevator.

By the time I got to the elevator, Precious was gone. She somehow made it through the crowded lobby and took off into the Mississippi night with a broken heart as big as the Natchez trace. Damn, I never will understand women. they'll throw themselves at musicians, then expect you to marry 'em, settle down, give it all up, and raise kids. Still something about Precious was different. I missed her already and wondered if she'd be at the big Mississippi Showdown tomorrow night in Ray Football Stadium.

Tonight, I'll sleep alone! That's good I thought. I need all of the energy and focus I can muster for tomorrow night I reasoned in my mind. The elevator doors opened onto the fourth floor and the party goers tried to shove their way in as I shoved my way out into the nearly empty hallway leading to the now-closed hospitality suite. I needed some rest, and did not want to worry about Precious Smith. Negotiating my way through the empty glasses and beer cans in the hallway was a trick I had learned at the Ranch Inn Lounge. Still, there was a stirring quietness in my soul that echoed the sounds of drink glasses raised to salute happier times of a most recent past. The reflected fragrance of her perfume mingled with the echoes in my mind and bounced off my inner senses like the sharp points of refracted light from a muddled mental prism.

The morning sun bounced into my hotel room through half-closed slatted Venetian blinds making stripes on the foot of my bed like some cross bars on a sideways prison room. I could still taste the Scotch as I cautiously made my way to the bathroom and clumsily reached for the Colgate toothpaste. Furiously, I brushed at the cob webs in my mind as if they were clinging to my upper molars. Brushing your teeth, taking a shower and going to the bathroom are some of the most underrated pleasures of this world I thought as I slipped on my highly-polished cowboy boots. Today's the big day. Win, lose or draw. I'm gonna leave my mark in Meridian, Mississippi, I vowed, closing the door and heading for the Davis Grill to find my one and only true supporter, Jimmy Stretch.

"How do you feel?" Jimmy greeted from the round table.

"Fantastic," I retorted, not wanting Jimmy to know I was anxious as hell this early in the day.

"You ready for the big night?" Claude Gray queried.

"Ready as I'll every be," I replied defensively.

"Mrs. Jimmie Rodgers will be backstage, and Ernest Tubbs' band will be the back-up for you three finalists," Jimmy said matter-of-factly. A shiver ran down my back as I thought of performing with the Texas Troubadours from the Grand Ole Opry.

Ray Football Stadium was filled to capacity. Over eight thousand Country music fans had come to see the final night show starring Hank Snow, Ernest Tubb and other Nashville favorites. As I paced back and forth behind the huge outdoor stage like a pent-up tiger in a cage, I thought the time would never come for me to go on stage.

Finally, halfway through Ernest Tubb's performance, he told the crowd that the time had come to present the three finalists. As I waited on the steps for the first and second contestants to finish, I felt a tug on my trousers leg. "Psst, hey, I hear you been doing my song in the contest," said this skinny-looking kid with an upturned face.

"Who are you?" I said looking down from my lofty perch on the steps.

"Roger Miller. You gonna do my song tonight?" he questioned.

"Nope. I'm gonna do Jambalaya," I replied.

"Aw come on. Do 'Billy Billy Bayou.' Besides, you've won so far with it, haven't you," he reasoned. "It's brought you luck so far and you don't want to change your luck now do you?" he went on.

"Oh, all right," I said. As I told Buddy Emmons that I was going to change back to 'Billy Billy Bayou,' he just nodded. He then played the introduction to my first song as the announcer called out, "The Cajun Sensation from Louisiana." The crowd went wild! Two songs later, I stepped off the stage confident that I had won the contest. I could tell the applause had been louder for me than anyone else.

Thirty minutes later a stunned silence fell over the audience as Ernest Tubb announced that Ken Mabry had won first place and that Jay Chevalier had come in second in this first annual Jimmie Rodgers Country Music Festival contest. I felt a slow choking feeling in my throat as Ernest came off the stage and told Mrs. Jimmie Rodgers that I hadn't won first place. She thought sure I did.

As Jimmy and I walked down the hall on the fourth floor of the Lamar Hotel, we encountered a very inebriated Harry Stone. "Hold up Jimmy. Just a minute," Harry slurred his words. "If it's any consolation to you, Jay, you only lost the contest tonight by one point. We liked to have never talked Owen Bradley into bringing you into second place. He had you rated twelve points ahead of everyone else. But you see we had to let a homeboy win it so that the city fathers will continue to have the contest here every year. You all understand, don't you?" he asked as his words slurred even more.

"No sir, we don't," Jimmy blurted out. "We thought it was supposed to be judged by applause alone and Jay won it hands down on applause," Jimmy went on.

"That's all right, Jimmy. I think I understand. Good luck Mr. Stone. We'll see you in Nashville," I retorted. Trying to hold back the hot tears as I turned and walked down the reeling hallway toward the RCA hospitality suite Jimmy said, "I'll be damned. We got beat by politics.

"Hell fire, Jimmy. I need a drink. I won that contest. I don't care if it does say second place on this little old dinky-ass trophy. I'll never believe in contests again, and I'm never gonna be second best to anybody again. I'm gonna have me a hit record before summer's over. You just wait and see," I half-cried out through choked back tears. My heart was breaking, but I wasn't broken. "I'll have the last word on this contest if it takes the rest of my life," I thought as I stepped into the hospitality suite and into Precious Smith's arms.

"Oh, Jay. I'm so sorry about tonight. You had the contest stolen from you, and I really didn't mean what I said about wanting Ken Mabry to beat you," Precious blurted as I put a finger up to her lips to silence her.

"Don't worry Precious. You don't ever lose if you don't accept defeat! I don't accept defeat so I didn't lose. Ken Mabry, the judges and the city fathers can kiss my ass! I'm going back to Louisiana and I'm going to be a star. You can bet on that. Right now I need a drink and some tender loving care. I just need to drink tonight out of my mind. You want to join me?" I questioned and stated all at the same time.

"You bet!" she said as she reached for the bartender's bottle to pour us a double shot of trouble.

Chapter 4

"Lit Up Like a Pinball Machine"

Applause like new wine will go to your head and lift you up to a dizzying stratosphere. There if not careful you will begin to believe you can walk on water.

A hit record will take you beyond that to a place among the stars. There if not careful you'll burn like a rocket.

Thank God for friends who show you where the stepping stones are. I was lucky to have such friends. Still the quiver in my soul at being Number One on the radio charts made my knees feel like I was standing in a bowl of Jell-O.

Leaving Mississippi in the broad daylight on the Sunday after the great Mississippi Showdown was neither the hardest or easiest thing I had ever done. Shaking the Meridian dust off my boots was one thing, but leaving Precious standing in the doorway of her home was something else. Somehow, I knew I'd never see her again. Driving off into the afternoon sun was reminiscent of the old Saturday night cowboy movies when the hero just rides away, then stops on a hilltop to look back and wave. As I turned the corner and looked back to wave, I could see the sunlight glinting off her sparkling red hair as she waved back furiously in the afternoon sun.

The night before played through the corners of my mind like a song as I raced my car toward the distant Louisiana state line and the mighty Mississippi River Bridge. Hank Snow's "It Don't Hurt Anymore" seemed appropriate, but not true as I was still hurting from the defeat of the night before. However, some of the edge had been taken off the hurt with the double shots of Scotch and the violent expressions of unbridled passion shared with Precious through the night. Lovemaking can be emotional, physical, psychological, spiteful, forgiving, guilt-free and guilt-laden and a dozen other adjectives that still won't describe it. I thought about this as I tried to drive Precious from my mind and come back to my Louisiana world. Maybe she was right after all about us Louisiana Frenchmen, I pondered. As I roared across the Mississippi River Bridge into the beautiful Louisiana sunset over green cotton fields, Precious, Meridian and the contest seemed years behind in my memory.

Damn, a skunk had crossed the road about the time I lowered my window to inhale the sultry Delta air! Just my luck, I thought. My first welcome home was the pungent odor of skunk piss on cotton leaves in the Delta twilight. Oh well, it could be worse. At least, I could still distinguish smells as one of my senses was still working after the bombardments of all my senses Saturday night with the emotional disorientation of losing the contest by one point. Hell, worse things have happened, I thought, as the stars begin to twinkle over the Louisiana countryside. Tomorrow, I'll set a new course. Tonight, I'll make plans and by God, nothing is going to stand in my way. After all, didn't Nat Vincent say "If you write a hit song they'll never forget you." That's the key. I need to write a hit song, I thought as the lights of Alexandria came into sight and my tires sang on the steel grating of the Red River Bridge.

After explaining the events and details of the past week to my wife, Gloria Don and my folks, I felt an urgent need to see and talk to Pee Wee. Of course, it all had to be explained again to Pee Wee's family. After about the third time describing it, I said, "Man, let's go get a beer."

As we got into the car, Pee Wee said, "Let's drive over to my cousins Dewey and Tiny Jenkins house."

Dewey had just returned from the Air Force and was full of advice. Tiny brought cake and coffee. I was halfway through my cup of black coffee when Dewey made the statement that would change my life.

"Hell, if you boys want to write a hit song, you ought to write something about Uncle Earl. While you were gone, his wife put him in two mental institutions. He's got more trouble than anybody. Matter of fact, I just came back off of a trip and all you could hear on the radio is the song "The Battle of New Orleans" by Johnny Horton or something about Governor Earl K. Long of Louisiana going crazy," he explained through a big mouthful of cake.

"By God, you're right. Give me that guitar Pee Wee," I said excitedly.

'Sing, Sing Louisiana Sing, Sing about the Battle of New Orleans
Clap your hand, and sing your song, just a little story 'bout Earl K. Long.'

It seemed to roll off my lips. I thought half out loud, "Damn, that's a catchy chorus."

'Talk about your Jackson, your Robert E. Lee
Sing about Davey from Old Tennessee
But way down south in the Bayou land
A modern Robin Hood is a' leadin' his clan'

Where the words were coming from I didn't know, but I knew they were hot as I excused myself and left the house. Dewey shouted, "Good luck and goodbye," as I drove off down the old dirt and gravel road. The words were coming so fast I had to stop and grab a brown paper lunch sack to write on.

'Drivin' around in a big limousine
Everywhere he goes, there's a great big scene
All of the folks come from miles around
Just to see the show when he hits town.'

I was nearly in Forest Hill, three miles away from Dewey's house, when the third verse came. So, I stopped on the side of the road and wrote:

'Drivin' around, settin' the state in a whirl
Sayin, "don't ya worry, just trust Uncle Earl,"
Climb on the wagon and grab yourself a hat
We'll all take a trip out to his Pea Patch'

As I pulled into the Midway community, halfway between Lecompte and Forest Hill, the fourth verse came flowing from my mind to my pen.

'Well, some say he's wrong and others, not so
The rest of the people, just don't know
But to this one thing we'll all agree
Ole Uncle Earl has made history.'

It had taken all of twenty minutes to write this song. I had never written a song so fast in all my life. I knew it was perfect, so I stopped on the side of the road, reached in the back seat for my guitar and rehearsed it until I had it fully ingrained in my mind. I knew the tune was catchy, but what I needed now was an audience to try it out on.

Leaving Lecompte, I headed for Alexandria looking for an audience to confirm my expectations that the song was an exciting moment in my life. I just couldn't wait to get someone else's reaction to my song. As I pulled into the outskirts of Alexandria, I saw a group of highway workers who were taking a break for lunch. They were sitting beside their big orange trucks under some huge oak trees on the side of the road. As I braked to a screeching halt and jumped out of the car with my trusty guitar by my side, they look startled. "Hey, you guys want to hear a new song I just wrote about your boss Uncle Earl?" I asked breathlessly.

"Sure, let her rip!" Someone replied beside one of the trucks. Three minutes later, they were all gathered around me clapping and saying I needed to get that recorded right away. Well, what better audience than a bunch of old highway workers, I thought. Then on the other hand, maybe they were prejudiced. However, time would prove that they were right on the money.

A struggling songwriter/singer without a record company is like a farmer without a plow. Plenty of seed, but no way to plant and till the crop. Little did I know, there was a new record label being formed in Shreveport, Louisiana. The founder, H. G. DeMarais, was married to a local hometown girl, Betty Andries of Glenmora. How we all got together, I still don't quite understand. It seemed more like fate than any-thing else. Jack Kay, Ambrose Williamson, Kenny Gill, Herman Lasyone, the Moses Sisters, and Tommy Strange along with me and Pee Wee, finally wound up in Eddie Schuler's Gold Band recording studio in Lake Charles for the final cut under the direction of DeMarais. The "A" side for our new record was to be "The Ballad of Marc Elishe," about the founder of Marksville, Louisiana. The town of Marksville, located in central Louisiana, was then celebrating their official sesquicentennial anniversary. "The Ballad of Earl K. Long" was on the flip side. After the celebration, I just knew disc jockeys would play the "Uncle Earl" side of the record. Boy, was I in for a surprise! They not only didn't play it, it was banned from any airplay by all the radio station managers because they thought it was political and that I had written it for our crazy Governor. No one knew, of course, that I was just a kid from the piney woods and had never seen a Governor in my entire life, except for former Governor

Jimmie Davis at the contest in Meridian, Mississippi.

This was a new road block for me! It was déjà vu Meridian-style, all over again; except that it was on a higher political stage and had nothing to do with a music contest. It was similar, because Uncle Earl was fighting for his political life and sanity. It wasn't until later that I realized what a great struggle the Governor was having. His was a struggle to survive and mine was a struggle to arrive. Either type is frustrating when you know you are right and deserve a better destiny than what fate is handing you.

DeMarais was stymied. As president of RECCO Records, he had talked his board into backing this song and nothing was happening. It was a frustrating predicament. It was at this key moment I turned to my old friend, Jimmy Stretch. If anyone could get my record played, it was Jimmy, I surmised.

After telling Jimmy my heartfelt story and asking him to help me, he said, "All right, get me some records. I'm leaving Sunday. I'm not promising anything, but I'll try."

"That's all I can ask," I said gratefully on that Saturday afternoon in Pineville. Little did I know that within seventy-two hours, my whole world would be turned upside-down.

As I lay in bed with my wife, Gloria Don, and my daughter, Jan, asleep in the next room, I felt like I was the luckiest man alive even though I had only two dollars in my pocket. My wife had been working hard to help keep me in college on the G.I. Bill and yet in my heart, I knew that it was she who needed to be in college. I just wasn't cut out to be a student. My mind was always drifting to the studios of Nashville and whirling around on some disc jockey's turntable, fantasizing about my hit records being played across the nation. Dreams can build or break you. They are like a two-edged sword thrusting you forward and cutting you up all at the same time. As I listened to the soft breathing next to me I wondered if the fire and desire in my heart for success in the entertainment business wouldn't consume us all. I was still wondering while half asleep and half awake when the dogs outside started barking like all hell had broken loose.

I looked at my watch. It was nearly two a.m. as I heard my daddy's feet hit the floor and step quickly down the hallway to the front door. Visitors this time of night usually meant someone had died or had been in a terrible car wreck, I thought as I slipped on my Levis. "Hey Joe, is Jay home?" I heard Bill Mixon's familiar voice greet my father at the front door.

"Yes, he is. Come on in, Bill and Gloria," my old daddy replied. As I stumbled into the bright light of the kitchen, Dad was already putting the coffee pot on the stove.

"What's up, Bill?" I asked quizzing.

"You are," he shot back.

"I'll say so," Gloria half-grinned sheepishly.

"What do you mean?" I questioned.

"Well, Jimmy Stretch just called the house and said to get you to Baton Rouge. Your record is breaking wide open and going crazy," Bill said, matter-of-factly.

"You gotta be kiddin'. Man ain't nobody gonna play that record," I retorted.

"They started it last night in Baton Rouge," Gloria broke in, "and Jimmy said to get you to Baton Rouge for a ten a.m. press conference at the Governor's mansion," she went. on.

"Man you all gotta be crazy," I said. "I just can't believe it," I gasped.

"Well, it's true. Get your clothes packed. You've got to meet Jimmy at the Bellemont Motel in Baton Rouge at eight a.m." Bill stated rather jubilantly.

"Hell, I don't have any money, Bill. Two dollar's all I got to my name and my wife needs that for gas," I blurted out.

"Gloria, how much money you got," Bill questioned.

"Five dollars," she said.

"Five. I've got two and that makes seven. Here take it. Go to Baton Rouge. You can't ruin this chance. You can pay us back later," Bill stated emphatically as my dad poured coffee. Everyone else joined us to see what all the commotion was about. Now, the whole household was awake and excited.

The sun was coming up in the east as I crossed the Old Mississippi River Bridge into Baton Rouge. My mind was still reeling, wondering if it was true that they were playing my record. How had Jimmy done it? Did he have to pay off someone? Was it for real or was this just a dream? My sleepy mind was beginning to get a second wind as the adrenaline rushed through my body at the sight of the Bellemont Hotel. Jimmy greeted my heavy rap on his door with a hearty handshake and a great big good morning smile like the cat who just ate the biggest canary in Louisiana. "Boy, you've got a hit on your hands," he exclaimed! His excitement was contagious as he began to relate the incredible story of the night before.

"When I got to Baton Rouge last night, I went over to WAIL radio to visit with my disc jockey friend, Bill Bessom," Jimmy stated. Then, he began the story that would change my life.

"We passed our pleasantries and got caught up on the latest happening in the music business when I casually asked about eight o'clock had he received a record by Jay Chevalier titled 'The Ballad of Earl K. Long.' He said that he had. I said 'Well, have you played it yet?' He said no. I said, 'Well, would you?' He said, 'For you, Jimmy, I will.' Evidently, he had not gotten the word from the station management not to play the record as he was the Sunday night disc jockey. Anyhow, the rest is history. When Bill dropped the needle on the record the phone lit up. He said, 'Well, it's playing.' The caller said, 'I know, but I didn't hear the beginning. Would you play it again?' This happened three or four times when he turned to me and said, 'I've never had this kind of reaction before, that they want me to play it again and again.' I said,

'Well, play it.' When the record was over, Bill opened the switch on his microphone and said, 'Ladies and Gentlemen, we've just played a new record by Jay Chevalier called, "The Ballad of Earl K. Long." Some of you want to hear it again. Tell you what I'll do. If I get fifteen calls in the next fifteen minutes, we'll play it again. Bill had barely got the words out of his mouth when the phone lines lit up like a pinball machine."

This happened again and again until finally Bill asked Jimmy, could he get some copies to give away on the air? "What do you have in mind?" Jimmy asked. "Well, let's call Western Union and see what is the cheapest telegram you can send and for the first fifty who send us a telegram, we'll give them a free record. "How's that sound?" Bill questioned. "All right by me." Jimmy agreed. Western Union said the cheapest telegram was one dollar and thirty-five cents. They could go to the store and buy the record for between fifty and seventy-five cents. Jimmy thought this would be a good test of the popularity of the record.

For two hours after Bill Bessom announced his contest on the air that Sunday night, the phone lines went totally dead. Finally in desperation, he turned to Jimmy and said, "I guess I really fouled up."

"Well, why don't you call Western Union and see if there are any responses," was Jimmy's logical reply.

Bill let the phone call to Western Union ring and ring when he was about ready to hang up, a voice said "Hello."

"Ah, do you have any telegrams down there for Bill Bessom or WAIL radio?" Bill questioned.

"Are you Bill Bessom?" came the irritated reply.

"Yes sir, I am."

"Well, I can tell you one thing, either you are going to have to shut that radio station down and come over here and help us take these telegrams or we're going to have to come up there and help you run that radio station. We're busier than a one-arm paperhanger," the Western Union man said.

Jimmy related the story to me gleefully.

"Two hundred phone calls and fifty telegrams are just hard for me to believe, Jimmy," I said as I paced back and forth across his room. I wanted to shout, jump up and down, and savor this feeling for the rest of my life.

"Get freshened up, we're due at the Governor's mansion at ten a.m.," Jimmy said, bringing me back to reality. Damn, what do you say at a press conference, I thought. This was moving too fast for me to think. Maybe that was good, I rationalized.

"I'm ready, Jimmy. Let's go. I started, giving my hair that extra little flick with the comb, as I surveyed my best hit record look in the tiny bathroom mirror.

"Hop in. Don't forget your guitar and those extra records," Jimmy reminded me dutifully.

The ride to the Governor's mansion seemed awfully short. The front of the mansion was immaculate and very impressive. But nothing had prepared me for the excitement of a Monday morning press conference, especially with a Governor who had just been released from two mental institutions. Hell, he looked sane to me, I thought as I observed him answering all of the questions that he was being bombarded with. There was just a brief introduction and since he hadn't heard the record yet he didn't seem to know what to say to me. However, Margaret Dixon, the editor of the Baton Rouge Morning Advocate and the rest of the reporters knew exactly what to ask. Did I write the song especially for the Governor? What was my background, age, birthdate, birthplace, and a hundred other questions relevant and irrelevant? When it was over with, I was drained. Looking for a way out, I wondered just how anyone could keep from going nuts if they had to do this all of the time. Jimmy Stretch took me by the arm and said we needed to make several more radio stations to keep the momentum going. Within the next forty-eight hours, Associated Press and United Press International would do national stories. Paul Harvey would quote my song verbatim on his noon radio broadcast and I would be thrown into the national spotlight. Within one month, I'd have my own room at the Governor's mansion and a job with the Chief Executive of the State of Louisiana. Like the radio stations' telephone lines, my life too for the next year would light up like a pinball machine.

Chapter 5

"Blaze of Glory"

I had never met a stripper before or been to a place called the Sho-Bar. The Governor introduced me to both.

Blaze Starr, who everyone said was the highest paid stripper in the world at ten thousand dollars per week, was the headliner at The Sho-Bar on Bourbon Street.

The Governor at age sixty-four claimed to be "The Last of the Red Hot Papas." Blaze was his passion, she was twenty-eight.

The Governor was anxious to get to New Orleans. I thought it was the pull of "The Big Easy" itself that was calling him to the glitter and glamour of this magical sin city of the South. Soon, I would know different. As we sped down Airline Highway toward the Crescent City, the Governor's spirits seemed to soar higher. He sure didn't resemble the same person who just four months earlier had been put into two mental institutions by his estranged wife, Blanche, and nephew, Russell Long, and some of his over-anxious friends. That's how he liked to refer to those persons who sided with Blanche's contention that he was crazy. Matter-of-fact, the Governor in his most recent stump speeches across the state was telling his constituents, "They say I'm crazy. Well, if I'm crazy now, I was crazy then and if I was crazy then, then I've been crazy all of my life and some of you must be crazy too 'cause you voted for me three or four times." This would always bring howls of laughter from the huge crowds that came to the political stump speakings. What he was saying in those speeches made so much sense to the voters and supporters that people were now saying, "Ole Earl's crazy all right, crazy like a fox!" He was right; most of them had voted for him three or four times in various elections and would vote for him again. Evidently, the Governor could feel the tide turning. He seemed happier at this

Photo courtesy of Winn Parish Enterprise and
Pea Patch Gallery, Winnfield, Louisiana

moment than at any time in recent memory.

Pulling up to the Roosevelt Hotel in New Orleans was always an exciting moment for me. The Roosevelt with all of its magnificent splendor was my favorite place to stay, mainly because of the opulent décor in the lobby and the wonderful big dance band orchestra in the world famous Blue Room. However, for the Governor it held a different meaning. At one time, his late brother, Senator Huey P. Long, and Earl had owned the Roosevelt Hotel. They had sold it to New Orleans businessman Seymour Weiss, Huey's confidant. The sales contract stipulated that suite 340 and 342 would be Earl's or Huey's to use "carte blanche" for as long as either one of the two should live. The first two days in New Orleans we usually spent in these handsomely appointed suites. The Governor had his refrigerator chock full of his favorite fruits, cold cuts, wines and liquors in Room 340. It was here that he held political court and entertained some of his more intimate guests. Room 342 was for me on this particular occasion.

After parking the car and running some errands, I stretched out on one of the twin double beds, fully intending to take a nap. With the drone of the TV set in the background, I had been half-dozing for about thirty minutes when the jarring ring of the telephone caused me to sit straight up in the bed. "Hello! Hello! You sleeping?" the Governor spoke gruffly in my ear.

"No sir," came my reply.

"Well, come on over here, I have something for you to do."

"Yes sir. I'll be right there," I snapped awake as the adrenaline started flowing through my body from the command of his voice.

"Come on in," the Governor replied to my knock on his door. Reaching for the extra key in my pocket, I opened the door, cautiously for some reason that was not quite clear to me. "Well, come on in, damn it!" the Governor declared jokingly. "I want you to meet Miss Blaze Starr," the Governor said. I glanced to my left and there standing in the bathroom with nothing on, but a half slip was the gorgeous red-headed bomb shell. The world's number one stripper and Queen of Bourbon Street Burlesque was not six feet from me!

Blaze nodded and I mumbled, "Howdy." She was combing her long waist length hair and with every stroke of her comb, her voluptuous creamy-white breasts thrust forward like a goose-stepping soldier on a German parade field. Gawd, they were big! I thought to myself.

Instantly, my gaze snapped back to the Governor who lying half-seated and propped up in bed against two pillows with nothing on, but a white shirt and a pleasant relaxed look on his face. Now I realized why he was so anxious to get to New Orleans. As he got up from the bed, the scene would have been comical, had he not been so serious in giving me my marching orders standing there with his shirt opened all the way down the front. He seemed completely oblivious to the fact that I was the

only one there with any clothes on. Later, I would learn this was typical Earl Long.

It flashed across my mind as to just what type of sex this sixty-four-year-old man had enjoyed with this twenty-eight-year-old red-headed fireball. My thoughts were quickly interrupted with a list of things he wanted done. "Take Miss Blaze back to the Dauphine apartments, she has to go on stage at the Sho-Bar at eight p.m.," he commanded. "After you drop her off, stop by the French Market and pick up some fresh peaches, plums, grapes, apples and assorted fruit," he went on.

"Yes sir," I said. "Miss Blaze, are you ready?" I questioned.

"You bet," came the reply from this fully clothed beauty of magazine cover quality. Unbelievably she was even more stunning fully clothed. With a skirt and sweater to match of pretty rustic fall colors, her breasts were even more pronounced. Had I not known better, they looked too big to be real.

We left the Governor standing in the middle of the room and stepped into the hallway headed for the third floor elevators, which were down the hall and off to one side in a little alcove. Across from the elevators were a matronly looking lady and a dapper gentleman who looked of East coast breeding. With them was a bell boy dressed in his finest. He looked like Johnny, the Phillip Morris cigarettes poster boy. He was dressed to the nines, even to the cap that looked like the famous cigarette commercial of the 40's. The lady and gentleman were patiently waiting for the bellboy to open their room with a key that didn't seem to fit. About this time, we heard a gruff voice hollering down the hallway, "Hey! Hey!" Blaze and I stepped back into the hall and there stood the Governor outside of his room thirty feet away, butt naked, except for his shirt which was opened all the way down the front.

The lady dropped her purse and clapped both hands to her cheeks. Her husband looked dumbfounded and the bellboy just snapped his key off.

Blaze hollered, "You old son-of-a-bitch! Get back in your room! Are you crazy?"

Earl jumped back into the room, peeped his head out of the door with fingernails gripping the door frame, he sheepishly hollered gesturing with his one free hand, "I just wanted to tell Jay not to forget the peaches!"

Blaze shook her head in disbelief. I grinned as I realized that I had just seen my first streaker literally jump into his room. Of course, to this day, I'm sure those people didn't know that was the Governor of Louisiana, unless the bellboy spilled the beans. Later that night as I saw Blaze do her torrid Bourbon Street strip act at the Sho-Bar, I realized why the Governor would risk everything for this "Blaze of Glory." She was truly the classiest and finest stripper I would ever see. She was as beautiful as a movie star and lived up to her introduction.

"It's Star Time. The Sho-Bar proudly presents, 'Blaze Starr.'"

Oh, by the way, I didn't forget the peaches. Upon returning, I found that Uncle Earl had already packed up all of the fruit in about a dozen individual sacks.

"Let's go," he said.

"Where are we going?" I asked.

"To the Sho-Bar!" he exclaimed.

"These came off of my Pea Patch farm. They're good for your health. Eat up," Uncle Earl would say as each bartender, waitress and even other strippers got a sack. I guess that's why everybody loved the Governor, he was always giving something away. Being with Uncle Earl was like Christmas 365 days a year. Bellboys, bar maids, waiters, nurses, cops, carpenters, cowboys, farmers and gamblers, everybody had a place in Uncle Earl's heart.

It was truly amazing. But as the Governor himself would declare many times from the stump speaking, "You ain't seen nothin' yet." I was beginning to believe it was true. I could hardly wait for tomorrow to come and the next exciting adventure for the Earl and I.

Jay Chevalier Collection,
Northwestern State University
Archives, Natchitoches, Louisiana

Chapter 6

"Po' Man's Jimmie Davis

Frozen fingers, ice cold guitar strings and a frigid stinging wind blowing off Lake Providence, just a few miles from both the Arkansas and Mississippi borders, caused me to wonder what else would I do for the Governor?

Damn, I'd give my front seat in Hell for a good four piece band and a stiff drink of Scotch whiskey, I thought as the Governor in his long black coat mounted the pickup truck bed stage. "Gimme the microphone!" he shouted. His next statement surprised me. . .

The wind whipping off of Lake Providence in the northeastern corner of Louisiana was bone-chilling, teeth-chattering cold! It was freezing my already stiff fingers to the strings of my expensive, handmade Martin guitar. As the icy sleet stung my cheeks, I tried to play and sing "The Ballad of Earl K. Long," one more time for this ragtag audience of would-be Louisiana voters.

It was ten a.m. on a dreadful dismal fog-laden November morning. This was a God-forsaken town filled with dirt poor farmers, sharecroppers and old age pensioners. We were so far north you could amost throw a rock and hit Arkansas. Why Uncle Earl wanted these votes so bad I didn't know! Hell, only a few minutes earlier, I'd been inside the only restaurant in town wolfing down hot biscuits, bacon and eggs and black coffee. While I was warm, I listened to Curt Siegelin and other members of our entourage swapping political war stories with the locals. This was a lot better than standing, shivering my ass off and singing in the back of this old red pick-up truck.

None of us had relished the thought of going outside to face this blue-cold north wind tearing at our eyes and freezing the breath with each word spoken. Outside the cozy restaurant, we could hear the loud speakers on the sound trucks as they worked the back streets imploring everyone inside the warm houses to come to the ten a.m. political stump speaking featuring Governor Earl K. Long and a political cast of thousands. As the music blared between the announcements, you could hear the record players' needle scratch across the surface of the old 33-1/3 vinyl plastic records each time the sound truck hit a bump on those world-famous Louisiana black-top roads and streets.

Old fashioned stump speakings, as they were called, are at least as old as the debates of Abraham Lincoln and Stephen Douglas. It was said that the term came from the candidates standing on a tree stump to be seen and heard above the crowd as they delivered their oratory. The difference between our stump speakings and Lincoln's is that we would borrow some locals' pick-up truck and the political speakers would stand in the back of the truck bed with the tailgate open. It served the same purpose as the stump; therefore, the term stump speaking, described very well a live outdoor political rally in Louisiana in 1959. Since I was the only singer, guitar player and entertainer, I stood on the back of the pickup for all the same reasons, to be seen and heard.

Now in this day and time, the sound truck, or in our case two new 1959 Ford station wagons, were invaluable. They were rigged with a record turntable on the front seat by the driver. On the top of the station wagon were four huge bell-type speaker horns. Two pointing forward and slightly outward and two pointing toward the rear. The power unit was hooked to the vehicles' battery and powered both the record player and public address unit on top. This way, the driver could drive down Main Street or back streets of any town while playing the current musical hits on the turntable that came out over the loud speakers on top. Every so often, he would flip the switch over to the PA system, slow down to about five miles per hour, and a thirty second live commercial would begin. He really was a rolling disc jockey, good humor man, and entertainment curiosity, all rolled into one. His pitch would go something like this:

"Ladies and Gentlemen. You don't want to miss it. The greatest political speakers of modern times. . . in person at the court house square, in just thirty minutes from now. . . come one, come all. . . Governor Earl K. Long of the Great State of Louisiana will be speaking along with former Governor Jimmy Noe, Curt Sieglin, Joe Arthur Sims, Speedy O. Long and many others. Free groceries, free cold drinks, free hams and turkeys will be given away. . . You don't want to miss this important rally! Uncle Earl will be speaking on the critical issues of our time. Come on out and hear the truth from the only three-time Governor of the Great State of Louisiana, Earl K. Long. That's just thirty minutes from now at the court house square at ten a.m. this morning. Now here's "The Ballad of Earl K. Long!"

Once the sound truck drivers made sure they had the whole town awake and excited, then one of the trucks would go on to the next speaking site in another town and start the ballyhoo all over. The other sound truck would then go to the local designated spot. There he would switch over to local electricity with a one-hundred-foot electric cord; usually he ran it into a local grocery store or service station, after asking the owner to use one of his outlets for ol' Uncle Earl. He would then set up one or two microphones and stands in the back of the borrowed pick-up truck. Usually, there would be one or two chairs put in the truck for Uncle Earl or the next speaker to sit on.

The rest of the speakers would work the audience until it was their time to speak. Shaking hands with everyone in the audience was a must and was done at every stop unless the crowd was entirely too large. If at all possible no one was ignored, everyone was touched. It was the political equivalent of an old-time tent revival.

As I continued trying to sing this live version of "The Ballad of Earl K. Long", I wondered in my mind what our opponent, former Governor Jimmie Davis, and his band were doing this morning. One thing for sure, I bet they weren't playing and singing in this freezing weather. He probably had his five piece band with the famous Moon Mulligan on piano and the Plainsman Quartet holed up in some warm hotel auditorium singing his big hit, "You Are My Sunshine." Yes sir, I bet I'm the only cold-ass guitar picker with a number one charted record in the whole world of show business freezing his rear end off this morning.

Glancing over my right shoulder, I saw the Governor heading for the pick-up truck. He really looked dapper with his long black overcoat and felt hat cocked at an angle. He had a lively quick step for a man who had been in two mental institutions just six months earlier. His sharp, short huffing breaths looked like the puffs of a miniature steam locomotive as he bounded up onto the tailgate of the truck.

"Let me have that mike! You done sung enough," he whispered hoarsely.

"Yes sir," I replied swiftly from the corner of my mouth. "And now, Ladies and Gentlemen, let me present to you the only three-time Governor, Earl K. Long!" As the applause and cheers begain to die down, the Governor's next statement floored me.

"How 'bout a nice hand for Jay Chevalier singing for you. You know he's all I could afford. I couldn't afford no big hillbilly orchestra. Just Jay. He's the Po' Man's Jimmie Davis."

Chapter 7

"Westwego Jail"

"You don't jack with the Governor," the state trooper said. Hell, I'd never heard of the Westwego Jail. But it turned out to be a long way from Sunset, Louisiana.

"You Are My Sunshine" was the request. Nope, was my answer. Dead silence was the result and the "Jail House Blues" was the destination.

By late Sunday afternoon in Sunset, the weather was just the opposite of Lake Providence, hot and sultry! Sweaty mosquito bites were about as irritating as the two drunk Cajuns who kept heckling and hollering for me to play, "You Are My Sunshine." These Cajuns, descendants of the French Acadians who had litterally been shipped out of Nova Scotia, Canada by the British, wouldn't take no for an answer.

We'd been on the campaign trail since Thursday. Four hard days of five-to-seven speakings a day. My throat was sore. The Governor could barely talk and tempers were on a hair trigger. All of us were ready for this last speaking of the week to be over.

Tonight, we'd go to the mansion in Baton Rouge and we'd rest up, then on to New Orleans for some R&R, Blaze and whatever else we could find.

"Play, 'You Are My Sunshine', damn it," the two hecklers just wouldn't quit. Must be Jimmie Davis' plants, I thought. Damn, I hate drunks, the thought raced through my mind. It hadn't been long ago that I'd been playing for the drunks at the Ranch Inn Lounge and any other honkytonk that would hire me. But this was different, I was a star now, or so I thought. I wondered why these two drunk fools didn't understand that.

These kinds of situations were always dangerous. I had recently taken to carrying a loaded pistol in the back of my guitar amplifier. Why can't people just be happy and mellow when they drink? Why in the world are they such fools after a few beers or shots of whiskey? Where in the hell was the Governor anyway? He was late again, as usual. Seemed like it was getting worse. It was always hurry up and wait. The sound truck driver had set us up in front of the local bar. Why, I didn't know? It might've been the only place with a crowd and electricity available, I reasoned as I sang another song to kill time.

Some of our tired speakers had quit the campaign trail earlier today, so here I was trying to make up for two or three missing speakers and waiting on the ever-so-late star of the show, Uncle Earl. I had sung every song I knew and was already starting over with my very limited repertoire of Cajun music.

"Hey! You gonna sing 'You Are My Sunshine?'" the two drunks slurred in comical unison. Well, it would have been comical except for me it was no laughing matter. I had made up my mind that I wasn't singing our opponent's hit song, PERIOD!

"Has Jimmie Davis been through here yet?" I shouted back over the blaring speaker horns.

"Hell no! He's coming through here tomorrow. We want to hear 'You Are My Sunshine' now, today, smart ass!" they shot back belligerently.

"Well, you can wait till tomorrow and get it from the original. . .coon ass!" I blurted out before I realized what a dangerous corner I had painted myself into. To say "coon ass" to a Cajun in anger was the equivalent of calling him a son-of-a-bitch. I should have known better.

To add insult to injury, I cranked up the volume on my guitar. Then I motioned

for the sound man to turn up his volume. With all the gusto of that famous beer commercial, I started singing "The Ballad of Earl K. Long." All of a sudden, there was
dead silence. My lips were moving, but no sound was being heard over the roar of the
crowd. My guitar was twanging loudly, but the microphones were as dead as last year's
new mown hay.

"What the hell!" I shouted to the sound man. "Did someone unplug the cord?" I
shouted again. He just looked at me and shrugged his shoulders questioningly.
"Damn it, do something. Don't just stand there, this crowd will go nuts if we're not
careful," I reasoned with him over the roar of this soon-to-be mob if we didn't do
something quickly. All of a sudden, I saw the crowd begin to part like the Red Sea for
Moses back in Biblical times. However, as darkness fell, on this Sunday evening, I
spied the flashing red lights of a State Trooper patrol car leading the way for our Lone
Ranger.

As I bounded off the pick-up truck and over to the Governor's car, he looked up
while peeling a peach with his rusty old Case pocketknife and gruffly stated, "What's
going on?"

"By God, Governor, we just lost all of our sound and this crowd's getting restless,"
I blurted out.

About this time, the sound man ran up to the car. "Those two drunk son-of-a-
bitches that wanted to hear 'You Are My Sunshine' just cut both of our good one hundred foot microphone cords with a pocketknife," he wailed to the Governor and me.

"Who done that?" the Governor said, eyes flashing.

"Those two drunks standing over yonder by that light pole. They've been heckling
me for an hour to sing 'You Are My Sunshine' and damn it to hell, Governor, I just
couldn't bring myself to sing it at your rally. I guess it teed 'em off so bad, they tried
to screw up our whole show and stump speaking," I reasoned as fast as I could to
those glinty steel-blue eyes of a Governor who was mad as hell!

"Get me those two troopers over here right now, Jay" he said between clenched
teeth. "We'll see how tough they are and if they're singing 'In the Jail House Now,'"
he grinned with a cocky amusing look.

As I saw the troopers handcuff the two drunks and put them in the back seat of
their state police vehicle, Uncle Earl mounted the back of the pick-up truck. A shush
fell over the crowd as Louisiana's greatest stump speaker began to rail the thick night
air with statements about how the Longs had built hard-surfaced roads so that these
barons of the bayous could drive out of the swamps and give their pirogues a rest. . .
How the Charity Hospital had saved the lives of many of their relatives, who were too
poor to go to a local hospital. . . How the Longs of Louisiana and Uncle Earl, in particular had arranged for free lunches, school books, paper and pencils for their children. . . How the old age pension, a product of Senator Dudley J. LeBlanc, of
Hadacol patent medicine fame and Uncle Earl, had comforted their mothers and

fathers in their golden years. These Cajuns of Sunset knew, they understood, and they voted Long all the way. The Governor was amazing. he gave his speech to an attentive audience with no microphones or sound system.

Now it's about a hundred fifty miles as the crow flies from Sunset to the west bank of New Orleans. The next day, I asked the state troopers what happened to the two drunks who had cut our microphone cords. "Oh, didn't you know? We took them on Uncle Earl's orders, to the west bank in New Orleans. More than likely, they are still trying to figure out where they are. I guarantee you, it'll be a long time before they cut another singer's microphone cord. And it's gonna be even a longer time before anybody finds them and they get out of the Westwego City jail! It don't pay to jack with Uncle Earl!" they grinned.

Chapter 8

"Blow Their Horn"

The Governor liked piano bars. He loved to try and sing. He sounded like a Louisiana bullfrog with a sore throat.

Here we were several blocks from Bourbon Street humming along with the piano player and his audience. It was then that the Governor slipped out of the bar room door into the black Mercury with no driver's license and a snoot full of whiskey.

A prime target for the New Orleans Police who had taken his driver's license several weeks before. The Governor was heading for Bourbon Street and I was hailing a cab.

Everything in life is relative to the moment, and circumstances leading up to an event are no exception. As we whirled off Bourbon Street in the big black Mercury into a quieter neighborhood of New Orleans, I could feel tenseness in the Governor's demeanor. He was trying to hum a song and guide me to our destination all at the same time.

"Turn down this street. Park behind that cab," he said hardly interrupting his croaking humming version of "Goody, Goody," a popular song of a few years back. "Let's go in. I know the piano player here," he said with a sort of detached look in his eyes.

I didn't know that he and Blaze had just had a serious argument back in her dressing room at the Sho-Bar. So I followed the Governor right on into the neighborhood pub with the belief we were just getting a late night cap. Inside was the typical New Orleans neighborhood cocktail lounge. A large baby grand piano-shaped bar and a cozy sitting area with high bar stools were around a better-than-average piano player who was the focal point.

Uncle Earl quickly straddled a stool, ordered a drink and requested "Goody, Goody" from the singing piano player. I sat on the stool beside him and surveyed the half dozen or so customers on the other stools.

'So you've met someone who set you back on your
heels, Goody, Goody!'

The piano player sang loudly as Uncle Earl joined in on the "Goody, Goodys" imploring everyone else to sing too.

'So you met someone and now you know how it feels,
Goody, Goody!
Hooray and hallelujah you had it comin' to you!
And I hope you're satisfied you rascal you!'

Uncle Earl seemed sort of mischevious and sad all at the same time. He loved music. Rumor was that he'd swallowed some lye when he was eleven years old and almost ruined his vocal chords. That along with a life of making stump speeches made his voice so hoarse as not to have any range for singing or carrying a tune. You could tell the music was in him, but it just wouldn't come out correctly. It was sort of sad, I thought, as I watched and listened to him try to hum, tap his foot and sing all at the same time. My mind flashed back to the house party in the Mathews' home with the rolled-back rug for the dancers and Uncle Earl enjoying me and Edgar Coco playing the music for the revelers.

"Play 'Bill Bailey Won't You Please Come Home'," he shouted to the piano man.

'Won't you come home Bill Bailey won't you please
come home. She moans the whole night long.
I'll do the cookin' honey I'll pay the rent
I know I done, done you wrong.'

As the piano man sang out with all of the verve that the shots of Jack Daniels had given him, the Governor asked me to go get my guitar and amplifier.

'Remember that evening that rainy, rainy evening
I turned you out with nothin' but a fine tooth comb
I know I'm to blame now ain't that a shame
Bill Bailey won't you please come home.

The piano man sang louder and louder as I stepped outside for my guitar. "Bill Bailey" and "Goody, Goody" were the Governor's two favorite pop songs. Maybe they reminded him of his estranged wife, Blanche or possibly Blaze, I thought as I started back inside.

"Folks, you all know who this is?" The Governor bellowed out as I sat back down at the stool. Without waiting for a reply he stated, "This is Jay Chevalier. He wrote 'The Ballad of Earl K. Long' and he's gonna sing it for you right now. Ain't you, Jay?" he commanded.

"Yes sir. Where am I gonna stand?" I said reluctantly.

"Hell, get up there on top this baby grand piano so they can see you. Give him that mike and stand, Mr. Piano man. We got a real recording star here and we ain't gonna charge you nothin' for the show," Earl boasted.

The piano man said, "Yes sir, Governor," as he handed me the microphone and stand. I then climbed upon the bar stool then on the top of the baby grand piano bar struggling and lugging the microphone, guitar and amp all at the same time. I felt about as useless as tits on a boar hog as the people looking up at me waited for the show.

I was so high on top of the piano that if I had straightened up all the way my head would have banged against the ceiling. How Uncle Earl could persuade me to get in these damn predicaments, I didn't know. It seemed we were always on the brink of some kind of comical disaster. With all of my former Marine Corps pride, it damn sure wasn't funny in the least!

As the tipsy bar-stool crowd looked up at me on this lofty perch, I felt like they could see every hair in my nose, not to mention, whatever condition my underwear was in. "Sing it, Big Boy!" one of the ladies squealed.

"Shake that thing!" another one yelled as her boyfriend or husband, I couldn't tell which, gave her a "go-to-hell" look.

"What key you in?" the piano player yelled.

"Whis. . .key, by God," I drawled. He grinned knowing the awkward position the Governor had put me in and there was just a faint look of sympathy in his eyes. The owner of the club was sweating blood. I assumed he was afraid of me scratching up his beautiful baby grand bar top. That's when I kicked off my shoes, gave a little Elvis twist in my sock feet and said, "Give me a C chord and let her rip!"

As I swung into,

> 'Sing, sing Louisiana sing. Sing about the Battle
> of New Orleans.
> Clap your hands and sing your song just a little
> Story 'bout Earl K. Long'

I felt a tug on my trousers legs. The crowd was going nuts singing along, dancing around their bar stools, swinging their hips and holding their glasses higher, as the others were clapping their hands and whistling! I guess this was the first time they'd ever seen a singing fool on top of a piano with the Governor of Louisiana pulling on his pant's leg.

"Damn it. Give me the car keys," the Governor said. I couldn't believe my ears. The New Orleans police had taken his driver's license some weeks before because of a traffic accident and he wasn't allowed to drive.

"What you want 'em for?" I whispered a shout and sung all at the same time.

"I got to get something out of the car," he mumbled. "Now give me the keys!" he stated with that icy-steel glazed stare.

"Yes sir, here they are." How I slipped my hand in my pocket, retrieved the keys, kept on singing, shaking my left leg and strumming my guitar all at the same time, I'll never know. It must have something to do with that old show biz adage, "The show must go on!"

I watched the Governor walk out the front door, with his coat over his left arm and his hat cocked jauntingly to one side. As the door closed, I had a sinking, shivering feeling go through my entire body. "Sing it Jay. Sing it again," the crowd clapped and hollered for the ballad.

"Thank you, folks. You been mighty fine. Thank you Mr. Piano Man and all of you remember to vote for Uncle Earl. I gotta go!" I shouted as I jumped down from the piano bar, a one-man bandstand, packed my guitar, grabbed my shoes and headed for the door.

Outside my worst fear was realized. The Governor of Louisiana was loose in New Orleans with no driver's license and driving a big black Mercury with a siren and no bodyguard to protect him. "Well, I've done it now," I thought. "I've crapped and fell back in it. How in the world am I going to explain to everyone else in the campaign that I let the Governor escape from me?" The thought raced through my mind. If he runs over someone in that big black tank, they won't stand a chance. That's all I need is either for him to kill someone or the cops to arrest him for no driver's license. It'll make every paper in the state and we'll lose the election for sure.

As I mentally kicked myself, my mind was racing in the wind for a solution. All of a sudden, a yellow cab appeared as if by magic. "Take me to Bourbon Street," I yelled as I flipped him a ten dollar bill."

"Where 'bouts on Bourbon?" he questioned.

I yelled, "Sho-Bar."

We'd been in the bar partying for so long that now daylight was creeping between the historic buildings of the French Quarter. As we pulled onto Bourbon Street and up behind a long line of cars with their horns blaring out in a discordant symphony, my heart sank. They were greeting the new day with honk, honk, whonk, whonk, honk, honk, whonk, whonk, etc. The cab driver let me out at the back of this honking, squawking stalled parade. I ran flying up the sidewalk with my guitar and amp flapping in the morning breeze. I ran past the line of cars with the drivers' invectives flying out of the open windows. "Who is that crazy son-of-a-bitch parked half on the sidewalk and half in the middle of Bourbon Street?" rang in my ears. If they only knew it was the Governor of Louisiana, they probably would think he was crazy!

As I threw my guitar and amp in the back of the car and eased into the right front seat I noticed a strange figure standing outside. The Governor barely acknowledged my presence as he continued to talk to this old farmer dressed in overalls. Evidently, he had wandered up to Bourbon Street from the French Market. The Governor and this character were deeply engaged in a serious conversation about planting peas, politics and the local weather.

The strip show had already closed at the Sho-Bar and evidently Blaze had gone home. If the Governor had left me stranded on top of that piano bar just to come back down here to patch things up with Blaze, he was a day late and a dollar short, I thought. "I'll be double damned," I exclaimed through clenched teeth. "Governor, here come the cops," I whispered breathlessly. Glancing out at the right side rearview mirror, I could see a New Orleans City police cruiser with red lights flashing. It was driving towards us, past the long line of cars It had two wheels on the sidewalk and two wheels out in the street as it inched its way along to the head of the line of stalled cars and pulled up abruptly alongside the leader of this stationary parade.

"Good morning, Lieutenant," I said as cheerily as I could.

"Who in the hell is driving this rig?" he shot back trying to see past my position in the right front seat.

"This here's the Governor, Earl K. Long," I stated with all the firmness in my voice I could muster in such a precarious situation.

"Oh?" he quizzed impressively.

"What can I help you with?" Uncle Earl said matter-of-factly to the now taken-aback, slightly-embarrassed and somewhat awed policeman.

"Governor, did you know you've got traffic blocked and backed up for several blocks?" the officers questioned good naturedly.

"Well, hell no! Why didn't they blow their horns?" the Governor questioned as innocently as a kid with his hand in a cookie jar.

"Officer, we're leaving right now. We're staying at the Roosevelt and I'm driving the Governor. It's been a long day and night of politickin' and I need to get the Governor to bed," I stated quickly. I sure didn't want this conversation to go any further for if it ended in a Mexican stand-off, we were really in trouble.

As I got outside and walked around to the driver's side, Uncle Earl moved over to the passenger's side. To my surprise, the New Orleans Police with flashing lights led us all the way to the Roosevelt Hotel, where the sounds of the blaring horns faded into the slowly breaking daylight drifting out over the Big Easy.

We'd barely escaped disaster one more time!

Chapter 9

"Billy Cannon"

It was a Halloween Saturday night. What happened in "Death Valley" at Tiger Stadium at LSU, on that fateful night was never before seen, nor since duplicated. It was a moment suspended in time that has seemed to forever linger in the minds of all who saw or heard the famous Billy Cannon run against Ole Miss that Halloween night.

Not only did Billy win the Heisman Trophy that year, but also I wrote a hit song which went to #1 and LSU went on to be the #1 football team in the nation.

I was there that night. I saw, I wrote and I recorded the "Billy Cannon Song." It would be five years before I met Billy in Colorado Springs, Colorado. By then we were both pros. But that's another story.

The stadium was filled to near capacity with a crowd of fanatic LSU Tiger fans. Coming on the field were their arch rivals, Ole Miss. Uncle Earl was sitting in the Governor's box on the fifty-yard line. I was restless and had found a vacant seat several rows back. This way I could keep an eye on the boss and the pretty young things who were scattered around in close proximity. When they jumped up and yelled, their poodle skirts flopped up revealing their well-rounded young bottoms. I had the best of both worlds, hanging out with the Governor and scouting the debutantes of the bayou.

It was October 31, 1959, Halloween night. Little did any of us know that within an hour and a half, something absolutely magical would happen out on the playing field. There was a full moon shining down on this modern day Death Valley, better known as Louisiana State University stadium in Baton Rouge. The roar of the crowd was at times deafening. The Governor seemed restless as usual. From time to time, he'd wander from his seat over to an old friend or stranger to shake hands and, of course, ask for that all-important vote. From my vantage point, all was well. However, I was wound tight as a coiled spring ready to jump to his side at the least sign of trouble.

We were less than a month away from the elections and each day and handshake was precious. The Governor never missed an opportunity to shake that last hand or to tell a captivating story that made him seem larger than life. To tell the truth, some of it was rubbing off on me and I was getting pretty good at shaking hands and asking them to vote for old Uncle Earl. From day one on the campaign trail, it just seemed the natural thing to do.

Back during the summer, the Governor had designed a grandiose plan to resign as Governor and then run for Lt. Governor. According to Louisiana law at that time, a Governor could not succeed himself. However, if he had resigned even for a few months he could then legally run for Governor in the fall of 1959. His friends convinced him that this would not work. The public would never buy it because everyone would know what he was trying to do. Instead, he had convinced Former Governor Jimmy Noe of Monroe, an old friend and ally, to run for Governor. The plan was for Uncle Earl to run for Lt. Governor on the Noe and Long ticket, therefore, keeping his hand on the pulse of the state. It was rumored that if Jimmy Noe won, Jimmy would then voluntarily resign and Uncle Earl would be Governor again. Crazy or not, the Governor was a genius when it came to politics, I speculated as my eyes wandered over this crowd. I wondered how many would vote for us.

Since the days of Huey Long, the LSU band had been as awesome and colorful as the football team. Playing "Hold that Tiger" and other famous rifts just made the night light up with electric emotions. On every play, the crowd was on its feet yelling, screaming, hollering and cursing when it didn't go our way. Forty-four thousand strong! Sure wish I had a dollar from each one, I thought. Seemed like I was always thinking of some way to promote or sell a record or further my career as an entertainer. God forbid that Uncle Earl might lose this election. What would I do if he did? Go back to Forest Hill?

Nowadays, things moved so fast, I hardly thought of Forest Hill, my mom and dad, or my wife and little three-year-old daughter, Jan. Sometimes, the Governor would ferry me from Baton Rouge to Rapides Parish, for I had left my car with my wife. He'd get the state troopers to carry me from parish line to parish line with my guitar, amp and suitcase. I was a high class gypsy. Most of the troopers liked my stories and giving them a free record helped. However, there were some who resented the fact that they had to give a free ride to this vagabond troubadour. No one dared let the Governor know how they really felt. Like it or not, many state employees served at the pleasure of the Governor. His was an unquestioning power. As the troopers remarked after the Westwego jail incident, "You don't jack with the Governor!"

Still going home for a day or two was anything but restful. Too many stories to tell, too slow a pace and not enough money to go around. My record company had gone out of business because they couldn't collect their money on the records sold. No one could believe I was sleeping at the Governor's mansion, the Roosevelt Hotel in New Orleans, and the Earl's Pea Patch Farm outside of Winnfield. Fact is, I had my own room in each location. As far as homefolks were concerned, I was just another local yokel. They were either jealous or just didn't think one of their own could make it to the big time! I had tunnel vision so it didn't make any difference what they thought. My immediate family was poor, but loyal and that's all that mattered.

As I watched the ball go from one end of the field to another and all of these crazy people around me screaming, cheering or booing, it just didn't seem to be that important. I never could get into football. Fact is, this was my first real college game to see. Forest Hill High School back home was too small for football. That was for big schools like the Bolton High School Bears in Alexandria. Shucks, we barely had enough players for our basketball and baseball teams. Come to think of it, there were only thirteen students in my graduating class in 1954 and half of them were girls. My interest in football was just about zero. Now girls and music was another story. Little did I know that was about to change.

Half-time came and the football game was locked in at a low score with Ole' Miss leading. The Governor ordered a hot dog with mustard and a Coke. I did the same while I wondered where we were going after the game. Probably back to the mansion, I surmised as tomorrow we would be back in Cajun country politickin' again. Sundays were always reserved for speaking in the Cajun Catholic parishes. The reason being, once Mass was over, Sundays were wide open to afternoon get-togethers in the local bars. Sometimes there would be afternoon and early evening Fais-Do'-Do's, the Cajun version of local dances. I always loved Sunday speakings in Cajun country. Pretty girls, good food, free spirit, good music, cheap whiskey and "Laissez Les Bons

Temps Roulé (Let the good times roll!) was the order of the day. Monday, it was back to hard work in the rice fields, oil patch or running traps in the swamps. But Sunday, that was like an extra Saturday. My mind was on tomorrow as the second half of the ballgame began.

When I was fifteen years old and growing up, I had a great uncle back home who said something to the effect that all women were alike. What I always thought he meant by that unfathomably profound statement was that all women were the same. I just don't believe he'd ever been to a LSU game. Matter-of-fact, I knew he hadn't or he would have revised that statement. Pretty girls were everywhere. Jumping, shouting and cajoling players too far away to hear their cheering for that touchdown. "Rah Rah Ree, kick 'em in the knee. Rah Rah Rass, kick 'em in the other knee," they cheered. Hell, that didn't rhyme on purpose, but I laughed anyway. As a song writer, in my world everything had to rhyme and stay on meter. Damn, I want to write a hit song that'll sell a million records more than anything else in the world, I mused. The thought was like a burning coal in my mind and down in my soul. For a moment, Meridian, Precious Smith and Jimmie Rodgers fiasco appeared in my reverie. It was disturbed by all hell breaking loose in Tiger Stadium.

I was on my feet now like everyone else. The punt from Ole' Miss was high, but it finally dropped into the arms of Billy Cannon like a misplaced feather. What happened next electrified a state, a nation and a twenty-three year old songwriter looking for his next hit. "Cannon got the ball on the eleven yard line. . . He breaks away" and then the announcers voice faded with the frenzied screams of the crowd. Legs pumping like pistons on a highballing freight train, Billy Cannon ran the ball back for an eighty-nine yard touchdown. That mystical, magical moment on October 31, 1959 would go down in LSU history books and be remembered and replayed by future generations every October.

As I looked around at this stadium full of screaming, hysterical fans, I could think of only one thing. So, I did the most logical thing for a writer in that electrifying moment. I grabbed for my pencil and wrote on the back of an envelope,

> "Down in the south where they say you all
> There's a man known as Mister Football.
> Billy Cannon, Billy Cannon
> Look out there he goes, Billy Cannon
> Here comes the ball a whirling down the field
> It's caught by Cannon and he's rolling like a wheel
> Billy Cannon, Billy Cannon
> Look out there he goes, Billy Cannon."

A moment frozen in time, with magic, to be captured every year on Halloween was a legacy for LSU that night. For this young, one-hundred-eighty pounds of dynamite went on to become All-American and a Heisman trophy winner and LSU became the number one football team in the nation that year. The song, "Billy Cannon" became number one on the WAIL Radio charts in Baton Rouge and overseas; and this kid from Forest Hill got lucky again.

BILLY CANNON OF LSU INSPIRES **RECORD** BY THIS 89 YARD TOUCHDOWN AGAINST OLE MISS..

Chapter 10

"Life In The Mansion"

It was a big step up from the outdoor toilet world of my piney woods home to the indoor modern plumbing of the United States Marine Corps in 1954. But it was nothing compared to the stepped-up lifestyle of living in the Louisiana Governor's Mansion in 1959.

Maids, chefs, gardeners, uniformed guards and a constant flow of political cronies, elected officials and guests from all over the state made the Governor's Mansion a beehive of activity.

At twenty-three years old, I had my own room at the Roosevelt Hotel in New Orleans, the Pea Patch farm in Winnfield and the Governor's Mansion in Baton Rouge. Life was good!

As we pulled up to the mansion, I could hardly wait to get to my room and put the finishing touches on my new song.

> 'You can go to the east, you can go to the west
> But everywhere you go they say he's the best.
> Billy Cannon, Billy Cannon. Look out there he
> goes, Billy Cannon.
> He's fightin' like a tiger, He's a runnin'
> like a light
> He's got the ball and he's got it out of sight
> Billy Cannon, Billy Cannon, Look out there he
> goes, Billy Cannon.'

Sounds pretty good, I thought as I set on the side of my bed strumming my guitar and matching chords to verses.

"You want some corn bread and buttermilk?" came the Governor's voice down the hallway.

"Yes sir," I replied, knowing there wouldn't be any use in saying no. The Governor was up so everybody else had to be up. His insomnia was getting worse. He barely slept four hours a night. You never knew if the four hours would be from ten till two a.m. or twelve to four a.m. The best thing you could do was to appease him. So long conversations would ensue with everything from old hog hunting tales to what you might think old so and so would do in this election.

At this time, the Governor was the only full-time resident in the mansion. His wife had left him to move over to a new home they had built but that he hated. He said it was on millionaire's row and it was too high-brow for him. I wondered what he thought the Governor's mansion was. It was damn sure a high class bachelor's pad if nothing else, I thought. The only two permanent guests were me and Senator A.A. Fredericks whose room was down at the end of the hall. Senator Fredericks had a way of ignoring the Governor at night, which was amazing.

As I stepped into the hall to make my way to the kitchen to meet the Governor, I saw the light under the door in Senator Fredericks' room. "How you Governor?" I said pulling my chair up to the table. "Great game tonight, wasn't it?" I added.

"Harrumph that Cannon's gonna go down in the history books. You want some of these mustard greens and field peas?" he questioned "Got some sweet taters too. . . I like 'em cold. . . There's some ham in the refrigerator. Get it out!" he commanded. Eating with the Governor was like a Southern feast fit for a king.

Soul food was everywhere, in the mansion, at the Pea Patch or the Roosevelt Hotel, but to him, there was nothing better than cold buttermilk and cornbread. I'd been raised on this kind of food. As a kid, I had hand-turned the buttermilk churn for my mama. After about thirty minutes, the creamy butter began to appear on top. Just as your tired arm felt like it was going to fall off, thick golden butter would appear floating on the top of the churn. These midnight snacks were beginning to put some weight back on the Governor. However, he still looked thin and frail for his size.

Despite his slight appearance, the Governor was tough as nails. A typical day at the mansion started with an early morning breakfast of bacon and eggs, grits, toast, biscuits, jams and jellies, Blue Ribbon cane syrup, hot black coffee and pancakes if you so desired. All of this was served by a staff that started coming in between five and six a.m. White starched linens and table cloths added to the elegance of this high-faluting male sanctuary.

All of the cooks and mansion servants were black inmates on special detail from the State Prison at Angola. Most of them were serving time for murder or armed robbery and either had very long or lifetime sentences. So duty at the mansion was really something for them to work for, and it was an honor. You had to be on your Ps and Qs to work for the Governor.

The Governor loved to tease them and have them show off for his guests at the breakfast table. One lady, in particular, was named Emma. One of her previous husbands had been a prize-fighter. The Governor would have her re-enact how he would go in the ring through the ropes, dance around his opponent with imitation feints and jabs. Then he'd ask her to demonstrate the fight in which her ex got knocked completely out. She would take the imaginary knockout punch and then fall to the floor immobilized amid the howls of laughter and applause from the eight to ten guests around the mansion dinner table.

Senators, Committee Chairmen, cronies and all varieties of hangers-on would make-up these morning breakfast meetings. The Governor always held court and was the center of attention. He never let anyone abuse or misuse the black servants and on many occasions, they were the recipients of much-needed gifts of extra money, food, medicine and clothing. Sometimes David Bell, a cousin of Uncle Earl's would show up. He was known as the Governor's big man. Evidently picking up money or delivering whatever the case called for was his specialty. Sgt. Butler was the Governor's bodyguard and private chauffeur at this time. He was almost always present. Other close friends who dropped by were Colonel Frank Odom, Senator B.B. "Sixty" Rayburn, Dick Davis and other cronies from all over the state.

Yes sir, this was the life! Living in the Governor's mansion with our own private barbershop, library, state troopers at our beck and call and meals like cornbread and buttermilk at midnight was the next best thing to a Southerners' heaven! How could you beat that?

As I watched the Governor eat his usual bedtime snack then pull his false teeth out and drop them in a cold glass of water, my mind wondered if this was all real.

Sometimes I thought, someone's going to pinch me and I'll wake up from this fairy tale-world.

The Governor's master bedroom was on the second floor. He rinsed his teeth, then wrapped them up in his pocket handkerchief and headed for the elevator. I waited for the elevator door to close and reopen on the second floor. Before going back to my room, I peeked in on Senator Fredericks. He looked up from the book he was reading and asked, "Everything O.K.?" I gave him the thumbs up and said goodnight. As I switched off my light and snuggled under the clean sheets, I heard the heavy pitter-patter of the Governor's feet coming back down the hall.

He walked past my room and toward the light coming from under the Senator's closed door. The Senator heard the Governor coming down the hallway. Quickly, he dropped the open book over his chest folded his hand and began a loud fake snoring. The Governor cracked the door and said, "Freddie! Freddie!" softly. Then louder, "Freddie! Freddie!" As the snoring got more pronounced, he said in almost a shouted hoarse stump-speaking voice, "FREDDIE! FREDDIE!" then uttered "Damn! Sleeping like a baby. Wish I could do that." He then turned and pitter-patted back down the hall in his old floppy slippers and cotton pajamas. The elevator door closed and opened again on the second floor as Louisiana's loneliest Governor went to bed in his heartbreak hotel. This ended one more day in the Governor's mansion of the very few days that were left for this three-time occupant.

Chapter 11

"Lost In Louisiana"

Tear drops make no sounds when they fall. Green grass grows quietly after the rains and Louisiana politicians never admit defeat. True to this nature, they pick themselves up after a close lost election and look down the road to the next race.

For it's in the chase and the race that the long shot always stands the chance to become the big winner. When you've been the Governor three times anything's possible. For Earl K. Long, dancing with destiny was not a new thing. It was just hard to tell who was playing the music.

Right now I was "Lost in Louisiana in 1959, somewhere between Hank Williams and Ponchatoula, Louisiana strawberry wine. . ." Sounds like a song, I thought.

We lost! Damn it to hell! We lost the election. It's all over, I thought. Chep Morrison won. Jimmie Davis came in second, Jimmy Noe fourth and the Governor came in third in the Lieutenant Governor's race. My whole world was turning upside-down again. I was hurting! My heart, my head, my mind was numb and my senses were frozen in time. Hell, if I was hurting like this, the Governor must be devastated. To his credit, if he was, he never did show it. "Always bet on a long shot," he said. "'Cause when they come in, they come in big," he said knowingly. I wondered if he'd ever be a winner again.

The blue and white Ford I had bought in the spring was purring like a kitten as I left Baton Rouge headed northwest for central Louisiana and home. I had a new record, "Billy Cannon," climbing the charts on WAIL Radio. It looked like it was going to be a number one hit. I had already passed Elvis, Fats Domino and Marty Robbins on the local charts. Things couldn't have been better except for one minor fact; I was out of a job and a steady income. Oh well, I'll worry about that another day, I thought.

Christmas time 1959 was coming fast and it had been a hell of a year. From the Mississippi showdown to the Louisiana slow down. My mind turned once again to Uncle Earl and losing the election. I wondered when I would see him again. He would be out of the mansion in a few weeks and there would go my free room, free meals and worst of all, the power I had come to expect from being associated with the Governor. What the hell, with a new hit record, I'd create my own power, I surmised. Still after all was said and done, that weekly paycheck would be hard to replace. I had no one to book me and still no telephone in the piney woods at my family's home to work on bookings or a career. Maybe Jimmy Stretch could help? My daddy worked hard everyday as a carpenter. Then, he'd come home and work till after dark trying to finish his own house. It was here, to that hard common everyday existence, I was returning reluctantly.

Driving up that old gravel road on this December evening in 1959, it seemed nothing had changed. But it was here also, that I could cocoon myself, lick my wounds and touch my roots with the luxury of a family who loved me dearly, a fact I had taken for granted. My mama Jewell, daddy Joe, sister Judie, wife Gloria and daughter Jan Dawn were standing in the yard and doorway with a thousand questions. Hugs and kisses, hot coffee and supper. . . God, I love this place! Still, there was a restlessness in my soul that longed for the next horizon.

Jan Dawn was even smarter than when I had left. She had a million questions and answers. She'd been an early learner. Almost too bright, you might say. It was scary sometimes. We would later learn she was a genius and she would become a member of MENSA, a national organization for the gifted. But for now, she was my little three-year-old daddy's girl sitting on my knee wanting to know where I'd been and why I'd been gone so long. The Governor and Baton Rouge were a million miles away, as far as this family of the piney woods was concerned. There was no real way for them to relate to my fifteen minutes of fame on the national scene or in the State's Capital. The mansion, servants, New Orleans, Bourbon Street and the Roosevelt Hotel's world-famous Blue Room were things of the recent-not-too-distant past. It was a time that would never come again. Or would it? Could lightening possibly strike twice? Hope springs eternal in the dreamer's mind and this night as I lay down to sleep, my dreams were of far away places, bright lights and big cities, not understanding I was holding the whole world in my arms.

My sister, Judie, had made friends with the local disc jockeys in Alexandria and was getting my record played. Jimmy Stretch was bringing me back charts from Baton Rouge and keeping me posted on my progress there. We'd go bird hunting with Dad and discuss what I should do. Jimmy was managing a young singer, Jimmy Elledge, from the Meridian, Mississippi, Jimmie Rodgers Contest. It looked like he might get him a contract with RCA Victor. I was on my own again. I had signed a one record deal with Jim Rentz and PEL Records of Baton Rouge. Jim was a helluva nice guy, but like all independents, he was underfunded.

I really needed to be with a major label, I thought as New Year's Eve 1960 was fast approaching. My mind drifted back to the present moment. We'd gone deep into the piney woods and cut a wild cedar tree for Christmas. The pretty decorations and the sparkling electric lights made shadows dance on the wall. Under the tree, the pretty paper and ribbons entwined the presents on this country boy's Christmas Eve. Caught up in an unguarded moment would be another delayed Christmas present, nine months from now.

As I snuggled deeper under the warm covers of the homemade quilts carefully and painstakingly sewn by my ancestors' hands, a song line kept running through my mind. It was New Year's Eve and I was already making resolutions that included New York, Nashville and Hollywood.

New Year's Day, 1960 and the tune just wouldn't go away.

> 'I got lost in Louisiana in 1959
> Somewhere between Hank Williams and Ponchatoula
> Louisiana Strawberry wine
> I got hooked on a feelin' that's kept me reelin'
> Deep down in my mind
> Yeah, I got lost in Louisiana in 1959.'

Pretty good, I thought. Maybe, I'll finish it someday. Right now, I've got a "Whole lotta' livin' to do," but where do I start?

Chapter 12

"Hollywood or Bust"

Hollywood had always been a dream of mine. Gene Autry, Roy Rogers and Tex Ritter were my heroes. That is until I wrote "The Ballad of Earl K. Long" then Uncle Earl took their place.

Still Warner Brothers Records was calling. So I gathered up all my courage, borrowed six hundred dollars from a local finance company and headed west.

Someone once said, God watches over fools, drunks and musicians. . . this time I fell into all three categories.

Hollywood! By God, I thought Norfolk, Virginia was the end of the world, when I was stationed there. Being a young eighteen-year-old Marine in 1954 lost in the Navy capital of the universe wasn't nearly as lonesome as being broke in Hollywood, California in 1960. The picture postcards of the stars' homes made it look so ritzy, so inviting, so tantalizing. Hell, they hardly knew who Governor Earl K. Long was and thought Baton Rouge was something to put on your face.

How had I landed in this cesspool of the cosmos? If they wanted to give the world an enema, they'd stick the syringe in Hollywood, I surmised on Sunday morning, coming down around the loneliest guitar picker north, south, east or west of the Mason-Dixon Line. There were no grits, no rice, no gravy, no biscuits, no deep dark-roasted coffee and no Southern comfort of any kind anywhere to be found in Hollywood. Just odd-looking people, bumming cigarettes and hitting you up for homosexual favors. God, where have all the straight people gone, I wondered?

Six weeks ago, back in Louisiana, it had been different. Just six weeks! Well it seemed now like six years! The phone call had come from Lake Charles. Eddie Schuler, owner of Gold Band Recording Studios, said that it might be my "big break." There was a promoter in town interested in a new song that I had written and left a demo tape of with Eddie. The song was international in scope. It was entitled, "Kruschev and the Devil." The promoter had contacts in Hollywood and thought he could get me a contract with Warner Brothers. "A probable movie contract would come with a record contract," he stated. That was all I needed to set my mind off on a star-studded tangent of tinsel town stardom.

But how was I going to Hollywood to even discuss this kind of deal? The Governor was out of office and the political dollars were all dried up. My occasional sock hop dances were sporadic and located far away in Baton Rouge. My band and travel expenses ate up most of the money from these small-time engagements. Still, I was going to find a way to Hollywood or bust!

A telegram arrived from Hollywood. Yes, they would like to see me in person at Warner Brothers and discuss a possible record deal. A possible deal? It was all I needed, so I walked into the Aetna Finance Company building in downtown Baton Rouge.

To this day, I don't know how I talked them into the six hundred dollar loan. I felt like the richest man in the world with those six crisp one hundred dollar bills. "Look out Hollywood. . . You ain't seen nothin' yet," as Uncle Earl would say. A pocket full of money and a new car barely a year old would make the difference in Hollywood, I thought. Throwing caution to the wind, I went home, packed my clothes and headed west, leaving behind upturned faces with questioning eyes that didn't even check my stride. After all, hadn't I just had two local hits in a row? Wasn't I now ready for the real big time? How could I miss? The telegram was from an address on Sunset Boulevard.

Sunset! By damn, that's the right name for it all right, I thought as my mind came back to the present moment. The sour smell of the old Oxydol washing powders filled my nose as my mind seemed to turn with each whirl of the commercial washing machine in the local washateria. I'd been holed-up in a local flop house for the past six weeks. It took Warner Brothers' Board of Directors two of those weeks just to make up their minds to tell me no to "Kruschev and the Devil."

Their reason was, it was a novelty record that had international implications and might start World War III! That was a chicken shit decision, I reasoned. And it was a cowardly position to boot. So to Hell with it, I'd make it some other way. Still, the chances were slim and none as I watched my shirt, socks and skivvies bounce around in the dryer.

I had passed a song publishing company a few days earlier that was named "Red River Publishing." Maybe, it had something to do with the Old Red River from back home, I thought. It was a long shot. Still, I opened the door and went in. I had seen the man behind the front desk in the Saturday night movies, or thought I had. The man behind the desk said, "Can I help you?"

"You sho' can. My name's Jay Chevalier and I'm a stranded songwriter from Louisiana," I stated crisply as I pulled my portfolio from under my arm and shoved it toward this potentially newfound friend. It held all of my newspaper clippings and PR credentials from back home.

"My name's Johnny Bond," he declared as he reached to shake my hand warmly.

"The same Johnny Bond with 'The Cass County Boys Band'?" I questioned almost in disbelief.

"The one and only," he replied. My knees were knocking. I had stumbled on a real movie star. Johnny was Gene Autry's band leader and had appeared in all of Gene's Saturday night B-movies that I had seen back home as a kid.

"Damn, Mr. Bond, you sho' are the first movie star I've ever shook hands with. Gene's my hero and I just love your song "Cimarron Roll On," I stammered trying to regain my composure.

"Thank you, Jay. This scrapbook is quite impressive. Most people don't get AP and UPI coverage, plus a Paul Harvey broadcast on their first record," he added very complimentary. "Come on back, let me introduce you to my two partners."

"How'd you get to Hollywood?" Tex Ritter drawled after Johnny had introduced me.

"It's a long story, Mr. Ritter," I said, feeling a little more at ease. Tex was a major motion picture "B" western star, but one of the nicest people I would ever meet. We would remain lifelong friends. Country and Western music would never have a classier gentleman than Tex Ritter.

After telling my story, Tex and Johnny introduced me to the "King of Strings," Joe Maphis. He was known to everyone around as the world's fastest guitar picker.

"What instrument you play?" he questioned right up front.

"Rhythm guitar," I shot back emphatically.

"Good. You want to work a job this weekend?"

"You bet," I replied quickly.

"It pays eighty dollars and expenses for three nights. Meet me at my house tomorrow. You can spend the night and ride with Rose Lee, me and the band to Jackpot, Nevada," he said as he scribbled his phone number and address on a note pad.

Cactus Pete's in Jackpot was the first gambling casino that I had ever performed in. Jackpot was located on the Idaho-Nevada state line about forty-three miles due south of Twin Falls. The tourists and out-of-town guests were filling the show room lounge as Joe went over the opening songs and keys they were to be played in. How I was going to bluff my way through this gig, I didn't know. Truth was, I couldn't play rhythm fast enough to keep up with Joe's flying fingers. I really didn't know if anyone could. I wondered if he knew that and had given me this job out of pity. Well, pity or not, I'll take the money. It was barely enough to get me back to Louisiana. That is, if I didn't mind driving straight through and sleeping in my car on the side of the road.

The three days flew by and we headed back to Hollywood. The show had turned out all right, but I vowed never to be a sideman again. It was hard standing to one side and not being a star and the center of attention. Joe and Rose Lee Maphis could not have been nicer. We would remain friends for life. However, this would be the only time we ever performed together.

As I got into my car and drove away, Joe and Rose Lee were standing in the doorway of their home waving. "I promise to write," I shouted out of the window as I headed out into the rising morning sun.

It was a hard two-day drive to Louisiana by the southern route across Arizona, New Mexico and Texas. That is, if you didn't dilly-dally along the way. This was no tourist excursion. I was headed home as fast as those six cylinders would take me. Freezing to death in the desert night and burning up in the west Texas heat with no air conditioner in this hot rod Ford was normal for June.

Angling north-eastward across the middle of Texas and hooking up on old Highway Eighty should put me in Shreveport around midnight, I calculated. As I filled up the gas tank, I counted my remaining change, which came to fourteen dollars and fifty-seven cents. With no breakdowns, I should be home by daylight tomorrow, I surmised.

"Welcome to Louisiana," the state line sign read. Straight ahead lay Shreveport and the famous "Louisiana Hayride." Hell, I might just stop and see DeMarais and Betty! Maybe I could get something to eat and see about a job possibility, I thought, as I fumbled with the knobs on the car radio. "Damnit where is KWKH?" I half exclaimed out loud nearly twisting the knob off in frustration. I was ready for some

Country music, Jim Reeves, Marty Robbins, Johnny Horton, Ernest Tubbs or something I could sink my musical teeth into. Hell, even Elvis, Johnny Cash or Carl Perkins with some rock-a-billy. I needed to hear some down-home shit-kicking music bad. What the hell! There it is, KWKH. "Yes sir, folks, that was former Louisiana Hayride star Elvis Presley singing his first big hit of yester-year, 'That's All Right Mama' and now for the news of the ARK-LA-TEX."

"Good evening, Ladies and Gentlemen. We have a red hot news flash from Baton Rouge, Louisiana. Former Governor Earl K. Long just announced today that he is running for the Eighth Congressional District seat which is now occupied by incumbent Harold B. McSween. And now for the ARK-LA-TEX weather forecast."

"Hell fire, I've got a job! Thank you, Jesus! God Bless you, Uncle Earl! We'll tear his ass up!" I thought as I tore through Shreveport heading south and home faster than Roy Acuff's "Wabash Cannon Ball!"

Chapter 13

"Where's Your Guitar?"

Louisiana lightening does strike twice! Here I was back in the singing and politickin' game in an even more dramatic way than before.

This time our campaign trail was confined to the eight parishes of central Louisiana. A place the Governor knew like the back of his hand. Plus, I knew every musician and night club owner within a fifty mile radius of Alexandria.

All we needed was me, my guitar, two sound trucks and some groceries to give away. With no Jimmie Davis band to compete with, we would make our own music and it was "The Ballad of Earl K. Long." This time, everybody would sing the song. Thank you very much!

I had slept through the day and around the clock after arriving home early Thursday from California. The sun was already up and the clock pushing ten Friday morning when I decided to go to Forest Hill four miles away to try and get some news on Uncle Earl. As I walked into the little country store, I spotted the stack of political flyers on the counter by the old fashioned cash register.

There it was in black and white, Uncle Earl's speaking schedule for the next three days. As luck would have it, he was going to be in Glenmora six miles away at four p.m. I quickly headed home to pack a suitcase for the next few days. My guitar and amp were still in the car trunk from the California trip.

"What makes you think Uncle Earl will hire you back?" my mother quizzed between sips of the coffee she was drinking.

"Because, by golly, he needs some music out on the stump and I'm 'the Po' Mans' Jimmie Davis.' He said so himself up in Lake Providence," I quickly replied. "'Sides all that, I'm affordable. Not cheap mind you, but reasonably priced to fit his budget," I added.

Mama laughed and nodded good naturedly. "Maybe so, just maybe so. But you must remember, you've got a pregnant wife and a little girl to take care of," she added emphatically.

"Yes, ma'am," I agreed. "Right now tho, I've got to catch up with Uncle Earl," I said pushing my chair back from the table and heading for the door.

The pine trees lining the stretch of gravel road from my house to the blacktop road leading to Forest Hill stood like silent sentinels guarding this secluded pathway to our old homestead. I had walked this road as a child in bare feet to catch the school bus. Then, it had only been two A-Model tire tracks through the woods and before that, log wagon ruts and before even that, an Indian trail. Once again, I was heading for a journey to God-knows-where and a date with Louisiana political history and the sunset of the Long dynasty.

Hell fire, Uncle Earl will hire me, I reasoned as I left the gravel road and headed west on the blacktop of Highway One Twelve. However, I'd better have a plan formulated, I thought, as I rolled westward under the late hot afternoon sun. I wondered who was working the sound. Maybe it's one of the Ellington brothers. They were my favorites. Ray and Jack Ellington, you could count on them to do it right. I wondered if I would see Dick Davis and Wilma Harris. They were friends and both savvy politicians. Dick was an old horse trader and deal cutter from way back, he'll be somewhere in the background, I'm sure of that, I thought as my mind wandered over the many characters that go into making up a successful political campaign. Someone once said, "In Louisiana it's horse racin' and politickin' and it's the sport of kings." I guess I agreed with that. One thing for sure, I'd rather pick and sing on the political trail than eat my mama's southern fried chicken on Sunday. Now, that's saying something, I thought. No doubt about it, I was hooked!

Uncle Earl was the best! Maybe the best stump speaker in the world. I'd seen a lot of stump speakers in last year's statewide race. Uncle Earl beat them hands down. From Jimmie Davis to Chep Morrison, he was the greatest of them all. No one could hold a light to him. Not even Senator Kennedy or Harry Truman. There was just something about him on the stump that was magical and electrifying, all at the same time. He wasn't elegant, he was dramatic and to the point, but able to cut through the political bullshit, right to the heart of the matter. His speeches hit you where you lived. In the pocketbook or tugging at your heart strings, Uncle Earl was the master when it came to reaching inside a voter's mind. All these thoughts were tumbling through my mind as I turned onto Highway One Sixty-five, a paved road headin' south to Glenmora.

Once I had fallen in love with a young Catholic girl from Glenmora. Nina Rose McNichols had stolen my young seventeen-year-old heart back in 1953. Now she was gone up north, some folks said. Back in the winter of 1954, I was in the Marine Corps and we were apart too long, so she sat down and wrote me my first "Dear John" letter. Hell, how could I expect her to wait? I had joined the Marine Corps for four years. But more than likely, it went beyond that. She was Catholic and I was Protestant Baptist and that was reason enough in 1954 in Louisiana for a "Dear John" letter. Both families were probably relieved, I reckoned, as I pulled into the Glenmora city limits.

Glenmora's first and only local Country music star, Diddle Babb, was leaning against a light pole as I pulled up next to the new fire station. Diddle had been my first music idol and inspiration. In the early fifties, he had a local radio show on KREH radio in Oakdale, Louisiana. Later, I had a show on the same station.

"Where you been, Jay? You know Uncle Earl's speaking at four? You gonna sing?" Diddle popped all three questions at once.

"I've been on the road hustling my new record, I know it and you damn right I'm gonna sing," I said as I shook Diddle's hand, he grinned from ear to ear. He was a former Marine and had seen action in the Frozen Chozin' battle of North Korea. There had always been a common bond between us. Besides, I liked all of Diddle's family. I'd even dated Sally, one of his good-looking sisters.

"How's everybody?" I questioned.

"Fine, just fine. Where's Uncle Earl?" he asked.

"He'll be here soon," I acted as if I had just left the Governor and no one was the wiser.

I needed to know who was driving the sound wagon. It was three p.m. and I could hear the sound man working the back streets of Glenmora. It sounded like Red Harkins or Ray Ellington, but whomever it was; he was doing a good job as the crowd was slowly gathering.

The pickup truck was already put into place with the tailgate down when Joe Arthur Sims, Uncle Earl's attorney and lead speaker, pulled up to the speaking site. "Damn, I'm glad to see you, Jay. You gonna sing? Uncle Earl's running late as usual," he said.

"Sure am, Joe. What time you want to start?" I asked.

"Well, the crowd's here and restless, why don't you kick it off, then introduce me, by that time, maybe the Governor'll be here," he stated matter-of-factly.

"Good enough," I agreed. I had always like Joe; he was a take-charge kind of guy. He gave the campaign trail some sense of stability; even if he did drink his whiskey and water by the quart from a Mason fruit jar.

As I mounted the back of the pickup truck, my mind was already spinning like a slot machine trying to figure out which songs to sing. Last weekend, I'd been at Cactus Pete's two thousand miles away with the fastest guitar player alive. What a contrast, I thought.

"Jambalaya," "Billy Billy Bayou," "I Thought I Heard You Calling My Name," "Cheatin' Heart," "Cold Cold Heart," "Mansion On The Hill," "In The Garden," "I Saw The Light" and now "The Ballad of Earl K. Long," were the songs I sang and played my heart out for this crowd of two hundred hard working people. A lot were friends or past acquaintances.

The crowd clapped and sang along. The brand new 1960 white Buick LeSabre eased up to the back of the audience. I caught a glimpse of the Governor out of the corner of my eye, sitting in the right front seat as usual. I quickly introduced Joe Arthur Sims and stepped down from the pickup.

As Joe Arthur tore into his long litany and roll call of the things the Long's had done for Louisiana and this part of the state, in particular; I carefully observed the Governor from a distance. I hadn't seen him in nearly six months and all of a sudden, I wondered how he was going to treat me. I didn't have to wonder long.

After a few minutes, the Governor pulled out his pocketknife and started peeling a peach while seated in the Buick. He finally looked up at me and motioned for me to come over to the car.

"Where've you been?" he questioned abruptly and gruffly!

"Hollywood," I snapped back.

"How'd you do?" he quizzed.

"Fantastic," I lied.

"Where's your guitar?" he mused.

"In the trunk of my car over yonder," I gestured.

"Well, get the son-of-a-bitch out and let's go. I'm running for Congress," he bellowed.

"Yes sir, you bet," I said grabbing his hand and pumping it so hard he almost lost the peach.

It was like I'd never left and Hollywood had never happened. Screw Hollywood. The Governor was the only solid thing I'd ever known in my life except for my family and the Marine Corps. Yes sir, we're gonna kick some ass before this one's over with, you can bet on that, I thought as I followed the Buick back to Alexandria and our new opulent base of operations, the elegant Bentley Hotel.

Chapter 14

"Old Dominicker Hen"

Earl K. Long was the best horse trader I've ever known. He was a great salesman who knew how to push the right buttons to get you to buy whatever he was selling.

This time he was trading an old dominicker hen and her little biddies that he said came from his Pea Patch Farm for approximately two hundred votes. The novelty of this trade: only he and I ever knew that the old hen was from just up the road within this community where she was hatched and raised.

The Governor's political genius knew no shame or boundaries. It never ceased to amaze me then, and it still does.

According to Uncle Earl, Louisiana's leading criminal attorney, Camille Gravel, was an arrogant little pissant. Ben Holt, Earl's former floor leader, was a whipper-snapper with a mustache that a cat could lick off and Harold B. McSween, well, he was just the incumbent congressman and a good licking would do him more good than anything. It'd help his mama and daddy and anyone else he came in contact with. Harold was born with a silver spoon in his mouth and you couldn't get it out with a crowbar. Earl told the crowd in Cheneyville, in central Louisiana, "He's got a mouth like a catfish. He's the only man I know who can talk out of both sides of his mouth, smoke a cigarette, whistle and lie all at the same time. Old Catfish-Mouth McSween, that's what he is." The Governor would describe his opponent at every stop in this manner. Finally, everybody in the Eighth District was calling the incumbent "Catfish-Mouth McSween." When the Governor hung a new moniker on you, it usually stuck. In this case, it stuck like glue.

The smartest and slickest trick I ever saw him pull was a few days down the road. Right now, we were headed to Leroy's for supper and a little rest and recuperation. The days on the road were long, rough and rugged. So Leroy's Steak House and Lounge became our favorite watering hole.

Leroy Chandler was a barrel-chested sort of a man and a typical lounge host. I always like being around Leroy because he had a way about him that made you feel welcomed. His steaks were the best in town and the lounge was located on the outskirts of Alexandria and had a kind of New Orleans atmosphere.

Matter-of-fact, on several occasions Leroy and I shared a room at the Roosevelt in New Orleans. It was rumored around town that Earl had loaned Leroy one hundred fifty thousand dollars to build his steak house. That may have been another reason we hung out there so often. However, the Governor always paid his bill with cash at the end of the evening. Six or seven of us usually would have steaks and mixed drinks with the tab being sixty to seventy-five dollars. The Governor would give me a hundred dollar bill to pay it with. He never asked for the change and I never gave it back. Sometimes, this was the only way I got paid in his last campaign. Although he had offered to pay me a hundred fifty dollars per week, he was usually two or three weeks behind. Times were tough and the money short because no one thought he could win this election. Therefore, the campaign funds were just about dried up and he was leaning on old friends for cash.

We seldom left Leroy's before midnight. It was always good to slip between the clean sheets at the Bentley Hotel. I had been with the Governor day and night for the last two weeks. He seemed to be relying on me more and more. I didn't know whether it was because he sensed the loyalty from me or just needed my young mind and strength to keep him going. Whatever it was, at night when we would finally go to bed, I was totally zapped, sapped and drained. How he could keep going was hard for me to understand. Everyone else on the campaign would slip away to rest and recharge, but I was trapped. I hadn't seen my family in days even though they were only eighteen miles away. If we weren't criss-crossing the sprawling Eighth District looking for votes, then we were headed for New Orleans looking for adventure.

I had spent twelve years in school and graduated. I had spent four years in the Marine Corps and had an honorable discharge. I had spent two years in Louisiana College before writing "The Ballad of Earl K. Long" and joining the Governor. I could throw it all in the Mississippi River compared to the education I was receiving in this last year with Uncle Earl. If he wasn't a genius, he damned sure had me fooled. Trying to cover his mind was like trying to catch the wind with a butterfly net. He was untrapable, unstoppable, unsinkable and the toughest human being I had ever met.

Still, there were times he would do things that just didn't make any sense at all in the present time. For example, we were on our way to New Orleans last fall with Smitty driving. I was sitting in the back seat covered up with hams, frozen turkeys and a bushel basket of peas while the trunk was full of tomatoes, okra and various other vegetables from the Pea Patch farm along with our suitcases, hanging clothes and the spare tire.

Between Baton Rouge and New Orleans, we passed a big stake bodied truck with Texas license plates loaded with hundred pound sacks of fresh picked corn, roasting ears as the country folks would say. All of a sudden, the Governor started flinging his arms about in the right front seat. "Stop! Stop! Stop him!" he said to Smitty as we drove past the truck at seventy miles an hour. By now, the Governor was leaning out of the window trying to wave the startled driver over to the shoulder of the road.

"God damn it, Stop him!" the Governor said to Smitty as he kept flailing his arms about. Smitty slowed down in front of the truck. The driver pulled over to the shoulder of the road. The Governor turned around to address me in the back seat, "Go see how much he wants for a sack of corn," he said.

"Yes sir," I replied, trying not to get killed by oncoming traffic as I stepped out onto the busy highway.

As I approached the Texas truck driver, he had the bewildered look of maybe being highjacked by Louisiana robbers. "Mister, you ain't gonna believe this," I stammered quickly, "but that's the Governor of Louisiana up yonder in that white car and he wants to know how much you want for a sack of your corn?" I said, trying to hide the grin forming on my lips.

"Is that Earl K. Long?" he said smiling.

"Yep, you got it," I replied.

"Hell, tell him he can have a sack, it's free. We like Uncle Earl in Texas."

I strode back to the car. "Governor, he said for you it's free. Said they like you in Texas. What do you think?" I asked.

"Here, give 'em seven dollars and tell him I want two sacks," he said pushing the money into my hand.

"Damn, Governor, where we gonna put this corn?" I said after dragging the two sacks back along side the car.

"Get that rope out of the back and tie it on top of the trunk," he said. Damn, seems like he always had a solution. After tying the corn on the trunk, we headed to New Orleans and the Roosevelt Hotel.

I hope to hell there's no newspaper photographers hanging around, I thought, as I put a bushel basket of peas on my shoulder and dragged the sack full of corn behind me across the lobby of the Roosevelt. Smitty was tagging along with a bushel of okra on one shoulder and dragging the other sack of corn. Uncle Earl was in the lead with a frozen turkey under one arm and a ham under the other. We looked like country-come-to-town as he walked to the front desk and got the keys to the suite.

Up in the suite, we parceled everything out in large brown paper grocery sacks. These were headed for the Sho-Bar tonight. Uncle Earl would tell the strippers, Polly Cavanaugh, the bar manager, and all the help how he brought these groceriees and vegetables to them from the Pea Patch. Even the corn!

This was another one of those present moments. We were halfway between Hineston and Leesville approaching the little community of Hicks when the Governor opened his eyes from a cat nap. "Stop! Stop! God, damn it, stop! Turn right here," he said excitedly. Damn, I wish the Governor wouldn't use the Lord's name in vain, I thought as I turned the Buick sharply into the long dirt driveway leading up to the old double-wide shotgun farm house. A porch spanned the entire front of the house. There was a net wire fence around a grass-free dirt yard that had been swept recently with an old-fashioned brush broom. Brush brooms were made of the limbs of the dogwood tree.

Sitting in the front porch swing was an older man in overalls. The lady of the house pushed open the front screen door and stepped out onto the porch, wiping her hands on her three-quarter length apron. It was one p.m. "Lordy mercy, Fred, it's Earl K. Long," she said to the man in the swing.

"Sho' is," he replied. "Come on in, Governor. We'll make some coffee."

Uncle Earl bounded up the old wooden steps, shook hands and took a seat in a straight-back, cowhide-bottomed chair, pushed back his hat and settled in. "Coffee sounds mighty fine. Make mine black," he told Mrs. Smith as she hurried back into the house.

As coffee was being served with homemade tea cakes, I leaned back against the post at the corner of the porch. I was sitting on the floor of the porch swinging my legs over the edge when around the corner of the house came an old Dominicker hen and seven little chicks. She was a pretty dark grey with hundreds of tiny specks almost the color of a guinea hen.

Uncle Earl spied her right away! "How much you want for that old Dominicker hen and the biddies? I been wanting one just like that for my Pea Patch farm up in

Winnfield, Mr. Smith," he said loudly.

"Why Uncle Earl, you just go ahead and take her. Just consider her yours. I just couldn't charge you for her. Nope, you take her on to the Pea Patch," he said gladly.

"No sir, Mr. Smith. I just couldn't take a fine hen like that for nothing. How about seven-fifty for her and the biddies. Here's the money. Jay, you go catch her," he said as he put the money in Mr. Smith's hands.

The deal was final, except for one thing. Catching the hen and biddies. For the next thirty minutes, I chased that old hen and biddies. Finally, we put her in a pasteboard box with holes in it so she could breathe. I then put her in the trunk and cracked it open so she wouldn't suffocate. We bade the Smith's goodbye and headed for Leesville, or so I thought.

Five miles down the road Uncle Earl said, "Stop! Stop! Damn it to hell, stop! Pull in right here." This time we were pulling up to Mr. Jones's house at two fifteen p.m. It was a replay of the Smith's adventure an hour before except for a minor change. As coffee was served, Uncle Earl was talking politics with Mr. Jones when all of a sudden he says, "Mr. Jones, I've brought you something from my Pea Patch farm up in Winnfield. Jay, go out there and get that old dominicker hen and them biddies for Mr. Jones.

"Yes sir, you bet," I routinely said. I was glad to get ride of that old hen. Mr. Jones was thrilled to death to have a genuine Earl K. Long dominicker hen from the Pea Patch.

For seven dollars and fifty cents, the Governor had just made two influential country families happy. Each one would tell all their relatives, one about selling Uncle Earl an old hen and the other about getting that old Dominicker as a present from Uncle Earl.

Yes, sir, for seven dollars and fifty cents, he'd just bought two hundred votes and the loyalty of the Joneses and the Smiths and all of their kinfolks!

Chapter 15

"Kansas City Kitty"

Sometimes I wonder why humans act or react the way we do. However, in retrospect it all boils down to our upbringing. We are an extension of our environment, families and school teachers.

So when I walked out on the Governor in Winnfield, Louisiana in July, 1960, I was as surprised as he was. But his action and my reaction to his request for the song "Kanas City Kitty" was a case study in my Southern Baptist church upbringing. There are some things that you just don't do in front of the Church during a revival.

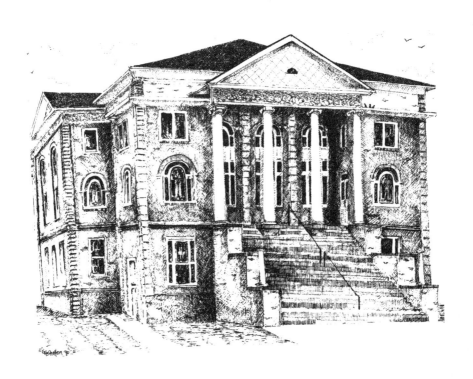

We're all born with three God-given basic instincts that are innate in every human being. They are paramount to human survival. . . fear. . . sex and hunger! At one time or another during a moment, minute, hour, day, week or year in each of our lives one or more of these innate characteristics becomes the dominant force that controls our actions or reactions.

Louisiana takes it to another dimension. With successful men in Louisiana in particular, there are the three P's which are: Power, Philandering, and Politics. Everything else being equal, the three P's are the driving force of powerful Louisiana businessmen and political moguls. Even the different religious factions of the state are touched and sometimes tainted by these three bonds of survival.

The First Baptist Church of Winnfield was having a week-long revival in July of 1960. Why Uncle Earl had scheduled a five p.m. political rally next door to the church was beyond me. Our crowd and the revival crowd were bound to meet before the seven p.m. church service. Besides all that, our political sound system would be blasting. The J.W. Thompson Country Music Band would be singing and playing loudly, everything from 'Hadacol Boogie' to 'Shotgun Boogie' plus every other honkytonk heart-breaking Country music song in between. This would be a strong and unsettling contrast to "Amazing Grace" and "Power in the Blood."

Normally, we should have broken down and left by six p.m., giving us a full hour before the church-going revival crowd arrived. It had been a hell of a day. It was Louisiana hot and July dry. The mosquitoes would be out soon, I thought. That would be another aggravation to put up with. Besides, the dripping sweat was running off my back under the short sleeve shirt. To make matters worse, it was also running down to the inside of my legs, and on down to my sweat-soaked socks inside my western cowboy boots. J.W.'s shirt was soaked wet with sweat, too. The Governor still hadn't shown up as six o'clock got closer.

While politickin' and picking music was still fun, it was hard work. Lots of days we'd make seven speakings. At every stop we gave away buckets of lard, hams, slabs of bacon, turkeys, sacks of groceries with beans, rice, flour and any other kind of staples country folks could use. This was standard procedure. It seemed like Uncle Earl was always trying to feed the multitudes.

It seemed he always had to give something away. The old Biblical verse "Give and it shall be given unto you" was practiced religiously. In all my life; I had never seen anyone practice this Biblical principle better than Uncle Earl. Aside from cussing, drinking, gambling and carousing, I guess Uncle Earl was just about the best Christian I knew. He said he was tolerant of all religions, Protestant, Catholics, etc. and even one of his secretaries was Jewish. He would hold up his graduation ring from Loyola University and say that if it hadn't been for the good Catholic Professors, he would never have received his law degree. Of course, he always told this story in the predominantly Cajun Catholic parts of the state. In central and north Louisiana, he would talk about his Baptist grandparents driving to church in a buggy on Sunday morning. Then he would add that his mother was a rock-ribbed Baptist. Yes sir, Uncle Earl covered all of the religious bases better than anyone I'd ever been around. Right now though, he was late and he was fixing to irritate the First Baptist Church of Winnfield's members. Plus, it was going to make him look crazy as hell!

Finally, he showed up. He crawled up on the speaker's platform and said, "Let Jay sing 'The Kansas City Kitty!'" It was six fifteen. The church crowd was parking their cars.

> "Well, I'm going to Kansas City
> Kansas City here I come
> Yeah I'm going to Kansas City
> Kansas City here I come
> They got some crazy little women there
> And I'm gonna get me one

I sang loudly. I felt so uncomfortable and sacrilegious. The Baptist ladies, all starched prim and proper, marched by with their turned-up noses. The men looked as if they were going to turn into a lynch mob soon. It wouldn't have surprised me if someone got a double-barreled shotgun and blew us all to hell, I thought as I finished the song. I whispered to J.W. to have the band play 'Missouri Waltz' which was less antagonistic to the religious crowd.

As the band played President Truman's favorite song, Uncle Earl's face screwed up into a frown. He looked like he was drinking Coca Cola, but I bet it was half and half. Half Coke and half Old Forester Bourbon, but in a coke bottle no one could tell he was really drinking a highball.

"Kansas City Kitty," the Governor hollered out over the band.

"I've already sung it twice, Governor."

"I don't give a damn, do it again! We need to loosen this crowd up."

"But Governor they're gonna be singing in the church pretty soon and it just don't seem right," my voice sorta trailed off as the Governor turned red in the face.

"God damn it, Let Jay sing 'Kansas City Kitty'!"

Well, that did it. I unplugged my guitar, packed up my case, picked up my amp and stomped off the stage headed for one of the sound wagons across the street. As I threw my guitar in the back seat, a startled driver said, "Where you going?"

"To the house! You can pick this wagon up in Alexandria. That's the last damn time I'm gonna be made an ass of. Worse than that, it just screws up my mind to see him act so damn stupid when he knows better than that. Just tell him flat out that I quit!"

I was fighting mad driving out of Winnfield headed for Alexandria. I'm damned sure not gonna stay around and watch the Governor lose an election over a drunk-ass stunt like pickin' and politickin' while church is going on, I reasoned. I guess I had really messed up. I didn't have a job. My wife was pregnant and Uncle Earl hadn't paid me in the last three weeks. Still, it was the principle of the thing. I'm damned sure not going to go crawling back. I ain't never seen Uncle Earl apologize to anybody. But I'm damned sure owed an apology. "Kansas City Kitty" my ass! Any idiot knows better than to sing a juke joint song outside of church, I reckoned. Well, just maybe the Governor is crazy, I thought. Maybe he is losing it. Of all the stupid things we'd done in New Orleans, still nothing came as close to being as bad as singing "Kansas City Kitty" during a revival meeting gathering.

I woke up in the back bedroom out in the country from a troubled sleep. Being out of a job was one thing, leaving Uncle Earl was another. "I'm not a quitter," I thought. Still, if the night before wasn't the most idiotic thing I'd ever seen I didn't know what was. Mentally and physically, I was still tired. Tomorrow would be Monday; today I would rest and make plans.

The black car glistened in the bright Monday morning sun as Dick Davis stepped out and walked up to the front door. "Mrs. Chevalier, is Jay home?" he asked.

"Why yes, come on in. I'll make some coffee, Dick," my mother said with concern in her voice.

Dick always looked dapper even if he was wearing a Hawaiian shirt. "Uncle Earl's looking for you, Jay," came the greeting from Dick.

"No shit! Well, I ain't lookin' for him," I replied.

"What happened in Winnfield? I've heard a couple of stories, now how about your side," Dick said.

After blurting the story out to Dick, he looked up quizzically and said, "Whatcha gonna do?"

"Nothing'," I said.

"Well, the Governor wants you to come back and sign that petition."

"Screw the petition. Tell him I'm printing my own damn flyer and it ain't gonna be pretty," I boasted and lied all at the same time.

"That's what you want me to tell him?" Dick asked reluctantly.

"You damn right and tell him it won't be long!" I shot back.

"All right, but don't do anything for a day or two. Just let things cool down," Dick requested.

"O.K.," I agreed.

Two days later, Dick sent word for me to meet him in town. "The Governor said he wants you to come on back. There'd be no hard feelings. That he'd give you your back pay and. . ."

"What the hell did you tell him?" I said breaking in on his to-the-point conversation.

"Just exactly what you said to tell," Dick replied with a grin.

"What did he say?" I questioned seriously.

"Well, he said, 'What do you think he's gonna put in that flyer?' I said well I guess some of that stuff you all had been doing in New Orleans," Dick laughed.

"No shit? Dick you told him that?" I laughed. The moment was becoming funny.

"You damn right," Dick said. "Now, come on get your stuff, let's go," Dick urged.

Sure enough, the Governor never mentioned the "Kansas City Kitty" incident again. True to his word, my back pay was caught up and we took off, rolling down the campaign road as if nothing had ever happened.

The Governor wasn't crazy, it was the Old Forester and Coke that made him not use good judgment, I reasoned. It seemed now that since I had stood up to him, he had a new respect for me, and "The Ballad of Earl K. Long." From now until the end of the campaign, I would never leave his side again.

Chapter 16

"Big Bad Bet"

"When you bet, always bet on a long shot because when they win, they win big,"
Earl K. Long said in 1959.

The Governor and Glen Lowe put up five thousand dollars each with Charlie D'Amico
in Alexandria. Glen bet the Governor that the Governor would lose the Congressional race.
Before it was over, Charlie would deliver $25,000.00 in cash in a brown paper bag to the
Governor in his hospital room.

Since then I've always bet on "The Long Shot."

Who came up with the idea, I'm not sure. However, the bet went down and Charlie D'Amico was holding the cash in his big black iron safe at the Sportsman's Lounge. The Sportsman's Lounge was a favorite watering hole for the locals. It was located on Third Street in Alexandria. There was a rumor that big Charlie, the owner, was the local Mafia Boss. Whether he was or not, I'll never know. One thing for sure, he was an affable, likeable, typical-looking Italian. He looked like he'd stepped out of a Hollywood gangster movie. Always dapper and dressed to the nines, he could be trusted, I assumed, to hold the money. Later, that assumption would prove correct.

Downstairs, The Sportsman Lounge served a large respectable lunch crowd at reasonable prices. Upstairs, it was rumored, was where you could lay down a bet on anything from the East coast to the West coast. Football, basketball, baseball and, I supposed, horse races would be wagered on. Judges, lawyers, bankers, nurses, secretaries and the movers and shakers of downtown Alexandria all gathered for lunch at the Sportsman's Lounge. Occasionally, there would be some Pentecostal preachers, Protestant ministers, priests and different men of the cloth would drop in for the good Southern soul food lunch. Everyone seemed oblivious to the action upstairs, or rather preferred to ignore any rumors associated with the Sportsman.

The big bet came from oil man and entrepreneur, Glen Lowe of Tullos, LaSalle Parish in North Louisiana. The challenge was five thousand dollars that Uncle Earl would lose in the first primary by five thousand votes. Uncle Earl answered the challenge by covering the five thousand dollar bet saying he would win in the first primary by five thousand votes. There were some side bets for several hundred dollars that Uncle Earl covered also. All together, big Charlie was holding over twelve thousand in bets in that old iron safe.

Rumors were flying everywhere as we started closing in on the final days of the first primary. Dick Davis started acting a little unhappy. He had confided to me that the governor owed him thirty thousand dollars. I never quite understood what Dick had done to deserve so much money. However, I assumed it must have been something in the recent past that the Governor wanted accomplished badly. Evidently, Dick felt like it would be very iffy that he would receive the money should we not win this race.

Everyone was becoming edgy. Even the sound truck drivers were displaying an intensity that I hadn't seen before. We were all hustling to put up "Elect Earl K. Long" signs. Each one of us had hammers, nails, roofing tacks and extra signs in the trunks of our cars and in the back of each sound wagon. When we weren't on the stump speaking, we were climbing tall ladders up telephone poles or leaning against high overhanging tree limbs to tack up Uncle Earl's election signs. Sometimes, we'd make night runs and tear down the opposition's signs. You always made sure that no one saw you so that Uncle Earl could always disclaim he had anything to do with it. Which really he didn't. Most of us just took it upon ourselves to do it. Once you've ripped down signs, the best place to dispose of them was under a bridge or stuffed up in a culvert.

There were times I would catch some of our employees being lazy. They would be given several hundred flyers to put up in grocery store windows with Scotch Tape and some large posters to tack up on barns, fence posts, telephone poles or trees. Some would do a thorough and good job while others would stay out all day jacking-around and come home in the evening saying they had covered a certain territory. It was easy to catch them in a lie. The next day we would follow the route they had taken. Sure enough, if there were no signs up, we'd find our own material up under bridges or in culverts. Lots of times, these workers would be day laborers sent in by the opposition just to sabotage our operations. When we discovered this to have happened, normally we would declare all-out war with the night raids on the opposition's signs. This would tend to stop the sign pulling for a few days.

You could normally tell how much money a campaign had by how many ads appeared in the local papers and how many signs were up on the trees and poles. The more you could get up, the more you intimidated your opponent and his voters. Before the days of television, this was the "art" of the campaign.

Uncle Earl was a political master when it came to psyching out his opponent with printed media. Be it billboards, posters, flyers, radio spots or large newspaper ads, he knew exactly what to do and say. The large hams, frozen turkeys, large bags of groceries, gallon cans of sausages and lard at the stump speakings were the icing on the cake, the final nail, so to speak, in the opponent's coffin.

No one had matched us thus far in the first primary. J.W. Thompson and his hillbilly band along with me and "The Ballad of Earl K. Long" for live entertainment was a formidable combination. When you added the expert oratory of Willard Rambo [who had married Mary Long], Senator F.E. Cole, Representative W.K. Brown, Senator Speedy O. Long and Hammond Attorney Joe Arthur Sims, we became a steam-rolling political machine to be reckoned with. Couple all that with our support crews of Ray and Jack Ellington, Red Harkins, Ellis "Easy Money" Littleton, Dick Davis and his pipeline of political information and espionage, there was no way Uncle Earl would run second, I surmised.

But run second, we did! Worse than that, we trailed by almost five thousand votes. Damn, we lost the big bad bet! What in the world will Uncle Earl do, I thought?

I didn't have to think long. Earl told old man Lowe to let the bet ride for the second primary. Mr. Lowe took the bait. He figured he had a sure thing. Now, it really was a big bad bet of over twenty thousand dollars on the line. The Governor had to come up with another ten thousand dollars just to stay in the game and to win in the runoff. It looked like a long shot, well, what had he said about a long shot? "Always bet on the long shot, 'cause when they win, they win big," I remembered. Still, that theory wasn't enough to keep some of our cronies from jumping ship.

Chapter 17

"Jugs of Money"

Sometimes you hear a story that just makes sense. Everyone has always wondered what happened to Huey Long's original Deduct Box.

When Smitty told me the "Jugs of Money" story, I knew what happened to the Governor's secret stash. Now you will know too. So read on.

Dick Davis was gone! Jumped to the other side! Damn, I wished he hadn't done that! I really liked him. If anyone could hurt us, it was Dick. He knew all our secrets, plus a lot of our strategy. The opposition knew it too. Thirty pieces of silver or thirty thousand dollars, when a former friend sells out, it always hurts in more ways than one. I never knew or heard if Dick ever got compensated. That was a secret he would probably take to his grave, I reckoned.

Money was getting tight. I was again three weeks behind in my weekly pay and working harder than ever. With Dick gone, the Governor was now becoming slightly paranoid. He insisted I stay with him day and night. Twenty-four hour days were the norm. Racing across the Eighth District at eighty to a hundred miles an hour, while exciting, was taking its toll on me. Tracking and backtracking. Day in and day out with an occasional side trip to New Orleans, was wreaking havoc with our lives, our cronies, our schedules, and creating uncertainty as to the outcome of this last election. The Governor was relentless in his pursuit to win. He gave no quarter and asked for none in return. We were racing with the wind. Hell bent for election or for Hell itself, we were riding as if there was no tomorrow. We literally raced the clock and exhausted our endurance. I wondered, someday, there will be no tomorrow. God, I hope it's not soon. But there's always a date set with the end. I just wanted our The-End to be a win, one last time.

We were running out of money, groceries and things to give away. At Pitkin, we gave away loaves of Holsum bread and Cotton Brother's cakes. People seemed to sense the urgency with our music, speeches and quick departures. The Governor seemed to be slowing down some in his delivery. But he still packed the punch of a steam locomotive and the country folk were eating it up.

In Cottonport, in Avoyelles Parish, on this Sunday morning, the Cajuns had gathered early for the ten a.m. speaking. The bar and grocery store combination was already doing a brisk business. In the last few days, the Governor had taken to flipping quarters to the local kids off the back of the pickup truck where he usually sat in a straight back chair. The kids would scramble and tussle over the quarters hitting the ground or concrete pavement much like the little Mexican children of Old Mexico for tourist-tossed coins.

As I slowly eased the car up to the speaking site, the Governor peeled off a hundred dollar bill from the wad he was carrying. He casually handed it to me and said, "Here, go get me a hundred dollars worth of quarters."

"Yes sir," I replied wondering where in the world I'd find a hundred dollars worth of quarters in little ole Cottonport on Sunday morning. It was an impossible task. He didn't seem to worry that I might not be able to find even ten dollars worth of quarters as he stepped out of the car and I pulled off in amazement.

I knew the Governor would be all right as I went in search of the quarteres he had requested. He would go right to shaking hands and swapping stories. This always seemed to give him energy. As I rounded a small curve in the road, the idea struck me. Where is the local Catholic Church? That's the solution. If anyone will know where to find quarters, it will be the priest.

The church was beautiful. The priest was back in the rectory after service. As I sat down in the big overstuffed chair in front of his huge mahogany desk, he said, "Son, how can I help you?"

"Father, I'm on a mission for the Governor, we're having a speaking down on the corner at ten a.m. and the Governor needs some quarters!"

"Oh? What does he need 'em for, my son?" he replied.

"Well, everywhere the Governor goes, he practices the old Biblical principle of giving to the needy. Normally, we give away bags of groceries. But lately, he has been giving quarters to the children," I stated proudly.

The Father leaned forward abruptly in his chair with a seriously concerned look and said, "My young man, isn't that buying votes?" Oh shit, I thought. What am I going to do now? So close to getting the quarters and my bragging about Biblical principles, flaunting my Baptist college knowledge of the Bible was going to lose the deal. The Governor would chew my ass out! The thought cut through my mind like a knife. I could handle anything, but an ass-chewing from Uncle Earl this Sunday morning.

"Oh no," I said as I snapped upright in my chair. "You see the children and their parents consider these quarters souvenirs. They will keep them over the years with stories to tell about how it was given to them by the political legend, Governor Earl K. Long," I stated unashamedly.

"Well, in that case, how many do you need?" the priest smiled as he reached in his desk drawer and started to retrieve rolls of quarters.

"A hundred dollars worth, if you have them," I stammered gratefully. As I gave the priest the hundred dollar bill, he placed ten rolls of neatly wrapped rolls of quarters in a brown paper bag.

"Thank you, Father; you have really been a blessing this day. I shall never forget it," I said as I hurried toward the door.

"And bless you my son and the Longs of Louisiana. God knows, they'll need it," he stated in a foreboding way.

I raced back to the speaking, thinking Uncle Earl and I were two of the luckiest people in the world. Maybe the smartest! Fifteen minutes ago, I wondered where to get quarters, now I had a hundred dollars worth all rolled up in individual ten dollar rolls in a paper sack. This would make it easy for him to handle tossing the coins.

"Here's the quarters," I said proudly as I handed them to him. He didn't say thanks, where'd you get them, go to hell, kiss my ass or nothing. He went right to breaking them open and flipping them to the kids. But that was typical. I guess he just assumed I could do the impossible. God watches over fools, politicians and musicians,

I thought, and I guess I fell in all three categories on this Sunday morning in Cottonport.

> "Amazing Grace how sweet the sound
> That saved a wretch like me
> I once was lost but now I'm found
> Was blind but now I see."

The old hymn floated through my mind like a comforting refrain as I dozed off riding by Smitty in the old Mercury once again. We were headed back to Leesville and then on to Alexandria. The road was long and straight from Evans, but would soon dead-end at the main highway. Smitty was driving too fast.

"Hang on, Jay!" he hollered.

"Son-of-a-bitch!" I thought as we skidded through the stop sign and across the paved highway up the bank on the other side and came to rest in the middle of a bunch of pine saplings. Smitty shoved the gear shift into reverse and quickly stepped on the accelerator. We backed out almost as fast as we went in. "Damn it to hell, Smitty! You're going to have to slow down on these country roads you don't know, especially at night. You're gonna get us both killed and I ain't ready to go yet!" I emphasized as I wiped the summer sweat from my brow.

"Sorry man, I didn't know the road dead-ended like that," Smitty apologized.

"Well, the car's not hurt, so let's go, just take it easy," I gestured for him to head to Leesville.

"Whatcha doing up in this Klu Klux Klan country, anyhow? Black men like you can get killed up here in the piney woods," I questioned as we both laughed. I liked Smitty, just as I liked Emma and all of the blacks that worked for the Governor at the mansion and at the Pea Patch.

"The Governor wanted me to bring him a package from Baton Rouge and some clothes out of the apartment at the Pentagon Apartments," Smitty said calmly.

"How long you known the Governor, Smitty?" I questioned off-handedly.

"Several years," he replied. "Ever since I started working at the mansion, the Governor's always been good to me and everybody else working there," he went on.

"Were you working there when they took him to the insane asylum?" I queried.

"God, yes, it was a pitiful time. We'uns didn't know what to do. All of us had heard about it on the radio the next day. We just couldn't believe it. Tell you the truth, the Governor ain't never been crazy, strange maybe, but never crazy. Emma was crying, moaning and praying. Us black men, we were just cursing under our breath. We didn't know what to make of it. 'Till finally, he came back after a couple of weeks when he broke out of Mandeville," Smitty's voice just seemed to drift off in the pitch black night air of the west Louisiana piney woods.

"Did you ever see any big money at the mansion?" I asked, bringing Smitty back to our conversation.

"Well, I don't know what you call big money, but while he was in the insane asylum I packed money one night from the mansion to Mrs. Blanche's limousine in gallon jugs for thirty minutes. Some of the money was so old it was yellow looking," he stated matter-of-factly. "What happened to that money?" I hastily questioned.

"Never saw it again after that," he went silent.

I wondered if that could have been the money from back in Huey's days as Governor and Senator. It could have been the famous deduct box money, I thought as Smitty drove us through the black Louisiana night.

The deduct box money was rumored to have started with Huey. If you worked for the State, you deducted ten percent of your salary and sent it to Huey as a political contribution. That way, he didn't have to steal from the state, was how he reasoned it, I guessed. Plus, he would have all the money in the world to finance his huge campaign expenses. Hell, the church worked the same way, tithing. If it was good enough for the church, it was good enough for Huey, I supposed. I just wished we had it now. No wonder Uncle Earl was broke. His inherited stash had been ripped off, if Smitty was telling the truth. Hell, I'd be crazy too if someone had taken off with all my money. I was sure Smitty had told Uncle Earl this story. That being the case, no wonder he was pissed off at Mrs. Blanche. She was on millionaire row and he was on the back roads of Louisiana fightin' for his sanity, political survival, dignity and even his manhood, I was soon to learn.

Chapter 18

"Hot Wells and Horseshoes"

When we passed the Leo Miller's Jewelry display in the Roosevelt Hotel lobby, the Governor stopped. The gold diamond crusted rings shaped like horseshoes had caught his eye. He bought the six on display and ordered six more.

Later, I saw him give the rings away one at a time to Dr. Scott, Dick Davis, Red Harkins, and Joe Arthur Sims. Finally, there were two left.

Who would be the lucky recipients of these last two rings? At Hot Wells Health Resort, I found out on a hot Sunday afternoon.

The hot summer sun was already high and leaning into the late afternoon as we sat on the front porch of Dr. Scott's large two-story house. Next door, the little country hospital was located. Both home and hospital faced the main street and a lazy Bayou Boeuf that meandered its way through my birthplace of Lecompte. My mama had given birth to me in the quaint little hospital March fourth, nineteen hundred thirty-six. That was twenty-four years ago. "You were such a hard birth," she said. She thought she was going to die as my daddy held her hand and promised never to get her pregnant again. A promise he never kept, for my sister Judie was born nearly eight years later in this same hospital.

It was three-thirty p.m. as the Governor sat talking with Dr. Scott. They talked about local politics, the weather, farming, cattle and just about every other subject you could think of. Every once in a while, I would nudge the Governor reminding him we were due in Montgomery for a four p.m. speaking. Montgomery was a good hour and fifteen minutes of hard driving going north from Lecompte.

"Governor, we gotta go," I implored for the fourth time in the last thirty minutes.

"All right, in just a minute," he muttered as he turned back to continue his conversation with Dr. Scott.

It was three-forty-five p.m. when the Governor slipped his hand in his coat pocket and retrieved the little box. We'd never make Montgomery on time now, I thought. Sure hope Joe Arthur Sims and the rest of the gang holds the crowd. My mind worried over the predicament we were in and I knew it was gonna be a long afternoon and evening. My thoughts were broken by the Governor's voice.

"Dr. Scott, I brought you this horseshoe ring from Leo Miller's Jewelers in New Orleans. Thought you might like it," the Governor allowed as he handed the little box to Dr. Scott. The sunlight sparkled off the golden horseshoe set diamonds like the different lights of a kaleidoscope at Christmas time.

"My God, Governor, this must have set you back a pretty penny. You didn't have to do that. I just can't take it. Now go get your money back. 'Sides, you need all your money to win this campaign," Dr. Scott said as he thrust the open ring box back to the Governor.

"No way, Doctor. That's yours. That ring's for you. You wear it. If I ever need it back, I'll come get it, otherwise, it's yours. You've been a real friend and God knows, I need some here in Lecompte. Especially since Huey put that main road outside of town and made everybody mad," the Governor reasoned.

There was no arguing with Uncle Earl. Dr. Scott accepted the ring. He put it on his finger and I must admit, it really looked good. The Governor said, "Well we gotta go. We're late, good luck." I hurried to the waiting black Mercury while Dr. Scott stood waving on the front porch as we drove away.

"God damn it, let the hammer down, we're late," the Governor said.

"I've been telling you that for the last hour," I retorted. It had become hard to keep him on time. The needle was on seventy-five as we hit McArthur Drive in Alexandria.

"Don't slow down. Hell, run that red light! Pass 'em on the shoulder. Pass 'em on either side. Can't you drive? Damn it, we're late!" the Governor shouted. The needle was pushing a hundred, then a hundred and ten as we passed cars on both sides of McArthur, ran through two red lights, drove into the ditch, back up on the road, and squealed the tires as I caught pavement again. Damn, we'll have to slow down for the Red River Bridge I thought if we don't get killed before then.

We were lucky there weren't many cars on McArthur Drive. After crossing the Red River, I lined that big black beast out at one hundred and ten miles per hour, heading for Montgomery. It was quarter to five as I looked at my watch. As we approached the city limits, I saw him coming from a side road. Yep, it was the fuzz alright. When I passed the gravel road, he recognized the big black Mercury. There had been an APB on the radio to stop that crazy son-of-a-bitch who'd just come through Alexandria at one hundred and ten miles per hour.

As I glanced up in my rear view mirror, the sheriff's deputy was barreling down the highway coming behind me with his siren blaring wide-open and his red lights flashing like fireworks on the fourth of July. "Well, here he comes, Governor, I guess, by God, they're gonna lock me up," I said in a pissed-off voice. As I pulled off to the side of the road, we were already an hour and fifteen minutes late for our speaking.

"Let me see your driver's license," the deputy hollered from his quick-draw stance as he stood there with his hand on his holstered pistol.

"Yes sir," I replied handing it to him through the open window.

"He's from Lecompte," the Governor stated seemingly unaffected at the jam I was in.

"Uh, we're late for a speaking. I was trying to get the Governor there. Officer, if you'll just let me take Uncle Earl on into town, I'll do whatever you want," I stammered, scared, mad and pissed off all at the same time. I didn't know what else to say.

The deputy leaned over, looked in the car and said, "Good evening, Governor. Young man, the captain from the state troopers in Alexandria has put an APB out on this car. They clocked you doing a hundred and ten miles per hour in the city limits. I'm gonna let you drive the Governor on to the speaking while I radio and see what they want to do with you," he said as he gave me back my driver's license.

I drove away slowly and on to the speaking. The Governor got out, jumped up on the speaker's stand as if nothin' had happened. He didn't even make excuses for being late. I told Joe Arthur Sims what had happened and asked for advice. "Don't sweat it," he said. "You may never hear from them again," he added. To this day, I haven't heard a word about the wild ride. I guess the troopers realized Uncle Earl had enough troubles without arresting his 'Po Man's Jimmie Davis.'

Montgomery was a fading memory as we headed to one of my favorite destinations. Hot Wells was located about fourteen miles west of Alexandria in the piney wood hills. Driving out of the Red River Valley where Uncle Earl had declared, "The soil is so rich you can grow anything. Why it's richer than the Nile Valley," he had said on many occasions. Hot Wells was an abrupt change in landscape. It was late Saturday night and tomorrow maybe we could sleep in.

As I lay in the large porcelain bath tub with the hot mineral water up to my ears, this Sunday morning was the next thing to paradise, I supposed in my mind. The ritual here at Hot Wells was to take a hot shower, then a hot mineral bath, hit the steam room and then go to the cooling room for a massage and a cool down.

There were about six or seven massage tables. We all stood or sat around butt-naked waiting for our massages. Patrons came from all over Louisiana as well as some neighboring states to avail themselves at Hot Wells, Earl's pet project. He loved it here. I understood why as the smell of Witch Hazel, rubbing alcohol and the mineral oil combination wafted through the morning air stirred by huge electric cooling fans mounted atop large five foot pole stands. It just didn't get any better than this. The Governor always insisted I get the works. As good as it felt to my muscular twenty-four-year-old body, it must have felt really good to the sixty-four-year-old Governor.

He was always quiet during our stay at Hot Wells. The tension there seemed a lot less and sometimes completely absent from his life in this famous health spa. The rubdowns were complete and invigorating. Muscles relaxed that I didn't even know I had. Lying on my stomach as the experienced hands worked up my legs, buttocks and low back muscles seemed to make the cares of the campaign seem far away. The rubbing and kneading of the muscles relaxed everything, even my libido. I wondered if it affected the Governor at his age the same way. Maybe that was another reason he and many others loved Hot Wells.

We strolled back up the hill after lunch to our rooms for a nap. I drifted off into a much-wanted and -needed siesta. Then all of a sudden the jangling of the telephone jarred me awake. "Come over here," the Governor stated gruffly.

"Yes sir, I'll be right there," I replied. He was in the next room. Still something must be troubling him, I thought.

I always responded to the Governor when he called or spoke my name. Never did I ignore him or his line of conversation. But it puzzled me when he said, "Hand me those boxes." There were none in sight. I glanced all over the room quickly.

"What boxes, Governor?" I replied timidly.

"Up there in the dresser drawer," he snapped from the supine position he lay in on the bed. The late afternoon sun was drifting lazily through the window as I quickly stepped to the chest of drawers. I hurriedly opened the drawer. There nestled between pajamas, underwear and handkerchiefs were two small boxes. "Bring 'em here," he hoarsely demanded.

I quickly retrieved the two boxes and stepped to the side of his bed as he propped himself up against the headboard. "Open them up," he said. As I flipped open first one box lid, then the other, two beautiful horseshoe rings stared back at me from their velvet mountings. One was gold and the other white gold. "Which one you like?" the Governor questioned. My mind raced. There was a small diamond missing from the white gold ring. Each ring had eleven diamonds.

"The white gold," I quietly replied.

"O.K. You can have that one. Give the other one to Mr. Thompson. You think he'll like it?" he questioned.

"Yes sir, I'm sure he will. Gold is his favorite," I said as my insides trembled.

"Well, put the white gold on and wear it. It came from Leo Miller's Jewelers. It cost me two hundred and ten dollars wholesale. If you ever get hard up and have to hock it, I'll give you your two hundred and ten dollars back," he stated as if I had paid for the ring myself.

"Yes sir. Yes sir. You bet! I ain't never gonna take it off either. Thanks a million, Governor." That was all that was said. He had ordered twelve rings from Mr. Miller only six were delivered and I had one of the six. A treasured heirloom. Too important for words, this moment would forever be etched in my mind.

Yes sir, it didn't get any better than Hot Wells and horseshoe rings. I felt like Tiny Tim at Christmas. "God Bless us one and all." I remembered the lines from Charles Dickens, *A Christmas Story* and "God Bless you, Uncle Earl" was what I wanted to say, but the words just wouldn't come out. This was a man-to-man thing, I guess. It was just understood. The horseshoe ring was an important symbol of fidelity.

Chapter 19

"Semper Fi"

"Yours is not to reason why, yours is but to do or die, Marine. Do you understand that?" The drill instructor shouted in my ear on this God forsaken piece of sand called Paris Island. "Yes sir," I replied without blinking an eye. At eighteen years old, I understood our Marine Corps motto "Semper Fidelis" (Always Faithful).

When I met the Governor five years later at the still young tender age of twenty-three, I had already been trained by the world's finest. That's why I treated him as my Commander-in-Chief.

If he had asked me to jump off the Mississippi River Bridge, I would have asked him which side. In 1959, as it is today, absolute loyalty was a rare thing to find.

"It's a long old road that doesn't have a turn in it," my mama used to say. I guess she was talking about some of these rough Louisiana roads we were traveling on or maybe it was just a figure of speech. Either way, there were plenty of curves in these old roads.

As I was thinking about Mama and home, my mind began to wander over the past few months with Uncle Earl. Everyone I had met on the campaign trail had an Earl K. Long story. I guess you could just call them "Earl's Pearls." Kinda rhymes, I guess. Maybe, I'll write a song about stories, I thought. Some of the stories were very funny. Some pointed to the wisdom of Uncle Earl and some just didn't make good sense at first glance. However, if you analyzed each one, there was a thread of wisdom that wove its way through all the stories. Most of all, there was a sense of loyalty and a common bond among the story tellers.

Stories like "The Chinaberry Chickens," "Earl's Castrated Cat," "The Yellow Dodge," "Red Wreathed Roses," "The Wrong Hog," "Somebody's Good Huntin' Dog," "The Pentecostal Preacher" and "One Friend."

"The Chinaberry Chickens"

The first time I drove up to the Pea Patch outside of Winnfield, it was dark. Two state troopers followed Uncle Earl and me as we approached the old tin-roofed house. The troopers parked their official vehicle out front. We all walked in behind the Governor.

"Make yo'selves at home, boys," he said as he invited us into his humble, sparsely furnished old country house. "I'll see if we can't get us some cold buttermilk and corn-bread," he added as he headed toward the kitchen in the back.

I had noticed a large Chinaberry tree in the front yard as we approached the house. If you were facing the house, it was in the left-hand corner of the yard. It was also the favorite roosting place of Uncle Earl's yard chickens. At midnight, we still had not gone to bed. The Governor decided he wanted to catch all of the chickens in the tree and put them in a large wire chicken coop in the backyard.

That's how two state troopers in military pressed uniforms and a country music recording star got roped into catching the chickens on their roost. The Governor handed each one of us a flashlight and told us to shine the light in the chicken's eyes. When they were blinded by the light, we were to catch them by the legs. We then ran like hell to the back yard with a squawkin' chicken in each hand. There, we would throw the chicken in the coop and hurry back to get more from the tree.

Problem was the chickens were so frightened that they were flying up to the top of the tree screaming and squawking like all get out while two or three old cur dogs ran from under the house barking and raising all kinds of commotion. The hogs over in the hog pen got scared and started grunting and squealing. The cows started running and bellowing in the cow lot. It was a regular Old McDonald's Farm gone nuts!

Through it all, the Governor stood on the porch cussing and giving us orders like a football coach. "Climb up the tree, catch 'em by the leg, hold 'em tight, blind 'em with the light," the Governor yelled and cursed. While the frightened scared-shitless chickens shit all over the troopers and me.

We never caught all the chickens. But the next day, several of the ones in the coop were dressed and southern fried for Earl's hungry guests. The Chinaberry Chickens wound up in Uncle Earl's pot so I guessed all in all it worked out as the Governor planned. Maybe, it wasn't so crazy after all!

"Earl's Castrated Cat"

Former State Trooper Dickie Ray Nugent told this story. He said one evening, they pulled up to the Pea Patch. This was shortly after the Governor had been released from the mental institution.

Several cronies and Doctor Pratt accompanied the Governor on this trip. As the Governor stepped up on the front porch, he spied an old yellow tom cat. It seems this old cat had gotten every pussycat on the place pregnant. Every time the Governor came home, there was a new litter of kittens.

He was exasperated by this state of affairs. Too many cats. He decided to eliminate this problem. "Catch that damn ol' yellow tom cat," he ordered the troopers. "Bring him here," he commanded as the troopers snagged the cat for the Governor.

"Doctor, you ever castrated a cat?" the Governor asked.

"No sir," the doctor said quickly. Uncle Earl reached in his pocket for his old trusty rusty case pocket knife.

"One of you hold his hind legs. Now, you hold the front legs," he told the other trooper. "Stretch him out and hold him tight," the Governor said. With two swift slits and two clean cuts, the Governor cut off the balls of the old yellow tom cat while the troopers did their best to hang on to the squealing, screaming, scratching machine. To add insult to injury, the Governor dabbed the wound with a mixture of turpentine and motor oil.

"Turn him loose quickly," he shouted. The cat let out a blood curdling scream you could hear for a mile as the troopers turned him loose. He took off like a jet rocket and when he hit the top of the barbed wire fence, Dickie Ray said it "zinged" like a twenty-two rifle bullet had ricocheted off of it. That ended the problem of all the pregnant cats. Once again, Uncle Earl had gone to the heart of the matter with his trusty knife to solve the problem.

"The Yellow Dodge"

It was a pretty vehicle. Canary yellow and white. It was brand new. The Governor said he bought it for Polly Cavanaugh. He'd probably give it to Blaze before it was over with, I figured. However, he did like Polly. She was the Sho-Bar manager and the go-between for him and Blaze. The cover, so to speak.

Well, here we were in the new yellow dodge station wagon headed for the local airport fifteen miles outside of Alexandria. I had called ahead to Delta Airlines and requested them to hold the plane for Governor Earl K. Long who needed to get to New Orleans. They said they couldn't hold the plane, not even for the Governor.

"God damn it. . . Step on it. . . We're late. . . We're late," the Governor yelled as we barreled down the road at ninety miles per hour. "Stay in the middle of the road, that way you can go either way if you see a wreck coming," he shouted.

"All right!. . . All right!" I yelled back. "Hang on. . . I'll get you there," I hoped as I drove like a madman. The dodge wagon cut through the early morning mist like a yellow jet hugging low to the two-lane blacktopped road.

Up ahead was a long concrete bridge with high railings on each side. In the middle of the bridge in the right lane was a slow moving empty gravel truck. "Pass him. . . Pass him. . . Put the hammer down," the Governor instructed, putting me in the dangerous situation of passing on the bridge.

At the other end of the bridge and out of sight was a gravel road that turned to the left. This road led to the gravel pit that the old dump truck was heading for. As I gunned the station wagon to pass the dump truck, the driver began to turn the old truck sharply to the left onto the gravel road.

"Watch out," yelled the ashen-faced Governor. "You're gonna kill us all," he screamed as an unseen force helped me do the best piece of driving I had ever done in my life! Quickly, I applied the brakes, skidding sideways and turning down the same road with the old gravel truck.

As we both ground to a halt in a shower of gravel and dust, I heard the sickening crunch of the right back fender. I had stopped the station wagon in front of the driver's side dual back wheels. The wheels had cracked the back fender just behind where the Governor was sitting.

It wasn't the truck driver's fault. We had been in a blind spot where he couldn't see us in his left side mirrors.

Now he jumped out of the truck headed toward us like a raging mad bull. "What in the hell were you trying to do you crazy son-of-," his voice trailed off as he saw the Governor. He quickly checked-up and said, "You all right, Uncle Earl?"

"Yes. Yes, we're late, see you later, got to catch a plane," the Governor yelled and waved as I threw the wagon into reverse and took off to the airport in a cloud of dust.

Behind me was a stunned truck driver with both hands up in the air and an exasperated look on his face.

The plane was waiting. It had been held for fifteen minutes. I guess they decided to wait for the Governor after all. I put the Governor on the plane and came back to survey the crushed right back fender. "Guess Blaze won't get the new wagon this week," I thought. Right now, I need a drink, I thought, as I reached for the fifth of Old Forester under the front seat.

"Red Wreathed Roses"

This story happened while Earl was recuperating in a motel outside of Covington, Louisiana, just after he was released from the second mental institution. Dickie Ray Nugent (at this time a young state trooper) was assigned to a guard detail, whose duty it was to protect the distraught Governor. Dickie related this story and several others to me. He spent one whole week with the Governor and although he was only twenty years old, he said the Governor liked to have physically worn out all of them.

There was an oil company over in Lake Charles that Uncle Earl had evidently beaten up pretty badly on some legislation the company had been lobbying for. It sent a funeral van over with a huge wreath of red roses to the motel. The implication here, of course, was not complimentary, but rather, it insinuated that the oilmen wished Uncle Earl had stayed in the mental institution. But it was all right now for they figured he was as good as dead politically with the mental institution stigma attached to his name. They thought Uncle Earl would forever be considered crazy.

Young Trooper Nugent hesitated in delivering the roses to the Governor. The Governor, however, insisted on seeing the flowers and reading the card. He asked the trooper, "Do you understand the meaning of this?"

"Yes sir," he replied.

"Well, wrap the son-of-a-bitches up. I'll take 'em into New Orleans tonight," the Governor said. "Hell, Blaze likes roses. She'll enjoy them," he added.

As I reflected on this story, in my mind it just proved once again the Governor wasn't crazy then or now. This ever-thinking Uncle Earl was not going to let anything go to waste and he damn sure wasn't going to let this gesture get him down. The whole world would soon know he wasn't dead politically, I believed within my heart. We'd soon have some new roses and stand in the winner's circle once again. I calculated in my mind. Yep, a new winner's wreath of roses sounded good to me. "What goes 'round, comes 'round," Mama always said and I reckoned it was true.

"The Wrong Hog"

Red Harkins told this story on several occasions. It was hog hunting time in the piney woods and the Governor had come home to "bring home the bacon," as he liked to describe it out on the stump speakings.

Rounding up a herd of privately-owned feral hogs was properly done on horseback with good Catahoula Cur dogs to help. The hunting terrain ranged from hollows and hills, to creeks and river bottoms. Over hills, and through the woods, the chase wound up at a huge blackberry briar patch. The location of it was not fit for man or beast. The old boar hog had tunneled his way backwards into his lair and was holding off the baying dogs with swipes of his six-inch tusks.

To identify your own hogs from a neighbor's you used ear marks, recorded in the parish courthouse. My daddy's mark was a crop and a half crop in one ear and a split and an under bit in the other ear. It was recorded in Rapides Parish.

Uncle Earl's mark was similar up in Winn Parish. At round-up time, all pigs were marked and males castrated. When hunting hogs, you had to get close enough to recognize your own ear mark. Otherwise, running in the woods, all hogs looked the same, and you certainly didn't want to kill a neighbor's hog. That was stealing and akin to cattle rustling. It was punishable, in some cases, by hanging or a swift bullet.

On this hunt, Uncle Earl was riding a big old gray horse. As the Governor huffed and puffed and dismounted from the big gray, he shouted, "Let me shoot 'em. . . Let me shoot 'em." Someone handed the Governor a twenty-two rifle as he got down on his hands and knees and peered into the burrowed tunnel trying to see the old boar. The Governor had beads of sweat breaking out on his forehead big as marbles. Trying to get a clear shot at the old hog was next to impossible and trying to see the ear mark at this point was impossible. Weaving the rifle back and forth, the Governor finally found and shot his target right between the eyes.

Tension was high as the old boar was dragged past the now-subdued hunting dogs by another hunter. As the Governor looked down at the kill, he is reported to have said, "I'll be a son-of-a-bitch, I shot my own damn hog!"

"Recognizing his own earmark was too much for the old man. The Governor then had his first heart attack," Red stated. In telling this story to me, Red laughed and slapped his leg for emphasis.

"Somebody's Good Hunting Dog"

While it was possible that the hog hunting story may have been embellished a little, the old hunting dog story was experienced by me first-hand. Recently, we'd been driving through some back roads in Winn Parish when the Governor spotted something dart into the bushes at the side of the road.

"Stop! Stop, right here!" he exclaimed.

"Yes sir," I replied squealing the new Buick to a stop.

"Back up," he snapped. The stench was sickening as I backed up alongside a large dead animal carcass on the side of the road. Buzzards had recently picked some of the flesh away from an old dead cow. Her ribs were showing and maggots were working on her underside next to the ground.

"Catch that old hound dog," the Governor stated.

"Yes sir," I replied as I whistled for old rover to come here. Finally, after much coaxing, I got a piece of rope around the old black and tan hound's neck and led him up to the Governor's side of the car. God! How he stank! He had been wallowing in the old cow carcass like the maggots and tumble bugs on and around the old dead cow's body and he smelled like it!

"Throw 'em in the back seat. We'll take him to the Pea Patch. He's somebody's good hunting dog," the Governor reasoned. I held my nose and drove on to the Pea Patch with old rover smelling the car up to high heaven. I wondered then how I'd ever get the car cleaned!

"The Pentacostal Preacher"

Billy Nash of Pine Prairie, in Evangeline Parish, just south of Alexandria, told me the preacher story. It was told to him by the late Reverend George L. Glass, Sr. Brother Glass was serving as the Louisiana District Secretary on the Board of the United Pentecostal Organization in 1949. He was also pastor of the First Pentecostal Church in DeRidder, near the Texas border.

The Pentecostals had just purchased land and were in their first tabernacle at the campgrounds in the community of Tioga, in Rapides Parish. Attorney Julius Long, who was Earl's oldest brother, handled the legal work for the ministers in purchasing the property for the camp. The Pentecostals were excited about their new location as their camp meetings for the past years were held at various churches around the state. Now, they had a permanent home, the Tioga camp. However, a good road was still badly needed.

The Board of Ministers consisted of a superintendent, a secretary and seven other ministers called presbyters. They were elected from seven different sections of the State. Brother Glass as secretary obtained an appointment for the board to meet with then - Governor Earl Long in regards to building an upgraded road into the campground. The day of the meeting with Governor Long arrived and the ministers went to the Executive Office located in the Capitol Building, in Baton Rouge. When Brother Glass informed the Governor's secretary of their presence, she instructed the preachers to go directly to the Governor's Mansion in the old section of Baton Rouge, as the Governor was waiting for the men to eat lunch with him. Brother Glass replied, "Oh, we were not expecting him to feed us today." So with great expectations, they drove to the mansion for lunch with Earl Long, the Governor of Louisiana.

When Governor Long had seated all of the ministers, he looked around the table and, conspicuously, there was an extra empty chair. He said, "Brothers, would you mind if an old gentleman out in the waiting room eats with us? His name is John and he came down this morning from near Winnfield to get some help from me and I know he has not had any food."

Brother Glass spoke for the group and said, "Of course not, how un-Christian we preachers would be if we refused John to eat with us." The Governor then brought in John and held him by the back of his neck, "Now Uncle John, keep your mouth clean while you eat and do not use any curse words because these are Pentecostal preachers and this is about as close to Heaven as you and I will ever get!" The Governor had a twinkle in his eye. Everybody laughed nervously and Uncle John said, "Amen!"

"One Friend"

After running the Uncle Earl stories through my mind like a movie reel, suddenly I snapped back to the present moment. I remembered the time the Governor and I were on our way to Alexandria from Baton Rouge. The Governor had maintained a reflective silence for almost two hours. As I drove the new Buick Lesabre along at better than the sixty-five miles-per-hour speed limit, I wondered why he was so quiet. We left the city limits of Bunkie, with the evening sun setting at our left over the western cotton fields, and the eerie silence was disrupted by his gruff gravelly voice.

"You know when you die, if you can count your friends on this one hand, you've lived a great life," the Governor blurted out, holding up all the fingers of his right hand. "If you can count this many, you've been very successful," he stated as he raised three fingers. With one finger raised, he captured my entire attention when he said, "If you can count this many, it's been worth it."

My startled words leaped from my throat as I exclaimed, "Governor, what is your definition of a friend?"

"The same as the Bible's. Greater love hath no man than this, that he lay down his life for a friend," he quoted. "My boy, that separates almost everyone you know from you, including your aunts, uncles, brothers, sisters and sometimes, the mamas and daddys. For how many people do you know who would really step between you and a speeding bullet?"

He stopped abruptly and looked straight ahead at the oncoming headlights as the silence again filled the speeding Buick. My mind reeled inwardly back to what they had taught us at the Marine Corps boot camp on Paris Island, South Carolina. You never leave your wounded or dead behind. It's one for all and all for one. No matter how many Marines it takes, you bring your buddies back with you. You were to always protect the Commander-in-Chief, even with your life, if necessary. Semper Fidelis (Always Faithful). The Marine Corps motto slammed into my brain now with a new meaning. By God, the Governor was my Commander-in-Chief, I thought as I thrust my hand across the seat and shook his hand.

"Governor, I'm your friend. You can count on that."

I silently resolved then and there to be his one friend, not knowing the end was just a few days down that long lonesome Louisiana road.

Chapter 20

"The Zwolle Tamale"

I've always liked hot tamales. However, the Zwolle Tamale wasn't the kind you wrapped in a corn shuck and ate with a bowl of ice cream as a follow-up.

She had long burnished red hair and a voluptuous bust line that must have reminded the Governor of Blaze. I guess that's why he made the unwitting mistake of hiring her to work in the Alexandria Campaign office.

It wouldn't be long before she would have to be hidden for a surprising reason.

Big Bad Bill Dodd received his nickname from Uncle Earl years before as a political rival in a bygone campaign. In reality, he was born in Zwolle and lived in Oakdale, Louisiana. He possessed a very engaging personality. He had traveled in the past with the Governor in friendlier times serving as Earl Long's first Lieutenant Governor from 1948 to 1952. So I took it at face value when in a private conversation he said that Uncle Earl was like an animal when he wanted to carouse. He said when the Governor got to rutting like an old dog after a bitch in heat, it didn't make any difference where he was if the woman was willing, that's where Earl did the job. On the levee, on the ground or in the back seat of a car, it was all the same to Uncle Earl when the urge hit.

While I thought this statement somewhat strange, I didn't challenge it. For I had not known the Governor in those younger days, still, I liked the ladies and by golly what man didn't, I thought. Hadn't we chased Blaze all over New Orleans? The Governor must be a real stud to catch a strip tease starlet like Blaze Starr. She was pretty as any movie star I had ever seen. She made Rita Hayworth look like a beginner. Yes sir, the Governor must be hell on wheels in bed, I thought. However, I had never seen the Governor be anything but polite to all lady folk, as he liked to call them.

It never occurred to me that something else might be wrong. Why he had sent me after the Zwolle Tamale in the middle of the night. Now that was a story!

My mind raced back to the scene. We were northwest of Alexandria, barreling down the highway behind the front sound station wagon. Uncle Earl had been talking about the pretty girl from Zwolle. She had told him she was from a poor family. She had waited on us in the little country café in Zwolle, near the Texas border. She had long, auburn brown hair, sorta like Blaze's. She had a crossbred Indian-Mexican look with dark olive skin. She was striking all right. She was well rounded with a voluptuous full figure to boot. Her lips were brightly painted and fully curved, just like a lipstick model on a magazine cover. Maybe Blaze had been gone too long, I mused. Maybe the Governor did need a good romp in the hay. Hell, it might relax him and take some of the heat off the rest of us.

"By God, I'll just go get her for you," I blurted out as we whizzed down the moon-drenched highway. It was nearly midnight.

"When?" the Governor asked!

"Right now. . . if you want me to," I challenged.

"Hell, you wouldn't go this late, 'sides her old man would shoot yo' ass off if you drove up this time of night askin' about his daughter," the Governor chided.

"Hell, I won't," I shot back.

"You really would?" the Governor questioned, baiting me on.

"Damn right, I ain't scared of her old man," I bragged.

"All right, pass up Jack in the sound truck and pull him over to the side of the road. I'll ride on into Alex with him and you can go hire the 'Zwolle Tamale' for me. Tell her she can stay with our office manager, Mrs. Hooter," he stated flatly.

"Oh shit! He's tricked me again!" I thought. "This will be a helluva lot harder than getting those quarters in Cottonport. Damn! Why did I let my alligator mouth overload my mockingbird ass," I thought as I blinked my lights to pull Jack Ellington over to the shoulder of the road.

Later, Jack said as Uncle Earl got in his station wagon and they headed for Alexandria. "You know Jay Chevalier's crazy!" the governor said. "He ain't scared of nothin'! He's going to Zwolle to hire that little 'ole gal we seen yesterday in the café. Why, he'll get killed for sho'." Jack laughed as he told me the story later.

Right now though, it was no laughing matter. It was one a.m. as I pulled up to the service station in Zwolle. A grimy-looking tire repairman in overalls looked up from the flat he was toiling over.

"Hell, she lives right down the road. Then right at the first dirt road. Go over the railroad tracks and turn right on the next dirt road. Her daddy's house is the third one on the left with a picket fence. Watch out for the dogs," he shouted as I drove away.

I pulled up in front of the house. Both of my headlights on high-beam blazed across the front porch. I honked the horn once as I slowly cocked the Smith and Wesson .38 special on the front seat by my side. I then stepped out and hollered, "Hello. . . the house!"

Twelve mangy, mixed-breed Catahoula Cur dogs reared up on the picket fence in choreographed unison and started barking, howling, growling and snarling with fangs glistening in the car lights. The fence swayed back and forth with this menagerie against it. All at once, a hulk of a man appeared on the front porch barefooted and shirtless with one strap dangling and the other holding up his blue denim work overalls. He cut a striking figure with the double-barrel twelve gauge shotgun at the ready.

"Who is it and what you want?" he demanded in a no-nonsense tone of voice.

Never have I spoken so fast before or since. In a rapid-fire gush of words, I explained my business. "I'm Jay Chevalier. I work for Uncle Earl. He met your daughter yesterday in the café. He wants to give her a good job as a receptionist in his campaign office in Alexandria and then maybe help her go on to school and find a good permanent job," I rattled off quick as I could.

He lowered the shotgun. . . released the hammers slowly and said, "Come on in. How's Uncle Earl doing anyway, never thought he was crazy. Damn papers, just make up stories. Can't believe a damn thing you read. I'll make some coffee. Say yo' name is Jay?" he talked nearly as fast as I did.

"Yes sir. . . I wrote 'The Ballad of Earl K. Long' and Uncle Earl's fine and you're right, you can't believe a damn thing you read in the papers."

Man, we were on the same wave length, I reckoned as we sipped the hot black coffee.

"Come back tomorrow, Jay. I'll have my daughter here and you can take her to

Alexandria. I'm sure she'll help the Governor," he said. As we finished our coffee, I departed. It was two a.m.

Sure enough, I had the "Zwolle Tamale" in the white Buick heading for Alexandria the next afternoon by four p.m. By five p.m., she was in the back seat on a side road where we had pulled over. By six p.m., I delivered her to the Governor and Mrs. Hooter, freshly-coiffured and with a smile on her face. Uncle Earl was thrilled, but not for long. It was the first and only time I had ever laid one of his present girl-friends. But I needed to know that she would go and that the Governor wasn't wasting his time.

Willie Long pulled up to the speaking site several days later and broke the news with a grin. "Jay, you know that gal you got for the Governor from Zwolle?" he said kind of slyly.

"Yep, what about her?" I asked.

"Well, she's got a rap sheet a mile long. She's out on parole from Angola for writing hot checks," he smiled that silly grin. My insides ran cold, that's all the opponent needs, I thought, to get hold of this information and spread it around that Uncle Earl had a hot check artist working for him.

"What did the Governor say about that?" I questioned Willie.

"He said for Mrs. Hooter to hide her out at her house and not to let her come back to the campaign headquarters. He's gonna keep her out of sight and pay her until after the election. You know he's not gonna admit he's wrong." Willie laughed.

Pretty smart I thought, but still it was dangerous, too dangerous! The next time I saw the Zwolle Tamale was the afternoon before the last primary on Saturday. On that Friday morning, the Governor had sent me with two packets of money to the towns of Leesville and Evans. The large packet was for Sheriff John Craft and contained five hundred dollars to help pay for drivers and vehicles to haul voters to the polls. The second packet was for Evans and contained two hundred fifty dollars for the same reason.

It was nearly four p.m. when I returned to the Governor's room and knocked on his door. I could hear the scurrying around in the room as the Governor hollered, "Just a minute." Within seconds, the Zwolle Tamale opened the door and slipped out as I stepped inside.

The Governor was dressed only in his white shirt and nothing else. As he lay back on the bed, his slight smile of satisfaction glistened as the late afternoon sun streamed through the window of the hotel room. This seemed like a déja vu scenario, reminiscent of the first encounter I had with a naked Governor and Blaze. Part of his anatomy looked blue gray in color. It may have something to do with circulation, I thought as the Governor complained that he was not feeling too well. Hell, he ought to have felt wore out, especially if he'd just rock and rolled in the hay with the Zwolle Tamale.

Still, I was worried something didn't seem right this time. The Governor really looked haggard. Had I known the truth, I would never have left the room!

"The Secret"

It would be years later that Dr. John Paul Pratt would reveal "The Secret." We met in Covington, Louisiana for dinner in 1993. The good doctor said, "I just wanted to set the record straight. I've kept these thoughts for thirty-four years and it just doesn't matter now," he went on. "I didn't want to leave this world without the truth being known. You see, Blaze's only mission in life was to raise the dead!"

"What do you mean?" I questioned.

"Well, in 1959, I was a young intern at Tulane University Hospital in New Orleans. When the Governor was released from Mandeville, I was assigned by the head of the Psychiatric Department of Tulane to assess his case. I spent three weeks with the Governor. I made the now-famous western trip with the Governor. As we were traveling down the road one day with a state trooper as our chauffeur, I looked up in the rearview mirror and saw Blaze giving oral sex to the Governor. The State Trooper saw the same scene, but being the gentleman he was, he averted his shocked glance and stared ahead. That's what I meant by Blaze's mission was to raise the dead. You see Jay, the Governor was impotent," Dr. Pratt whispered as he leaned over the dinner table. "He confessed this to me one day and said it was about to drive him crazy," the doctor added.

"You mean he couldn't get a hard-on at all?" I blurted out bewildered.

"That's right, he wasn't crazy. Just sexually frustrated that he'd lost his manhood!"

Damn, now it all made sense. I had been traveling with the most powerful man in Louisiana, yet with all his political power it didn't transfer to his manhood. No wonder some of the things we had done seemed so reckless, so frustrating and so crazy!

The truth is an elusive thing. Secrets sometimes take years to surface. The difference between hindsight and foresight is the former is always twenty/twenty and the future is, at best, uncertain even on a clear day. I wish I could have seen the future on that bright Friday afternoon the twenty-fifth day of August, 1960. But I couldn't . . . No one could!

Chapter 21

"Eleven Days to Glory"

When you've been to the mountain top, it's hard to go back to the valley. For eleven days, I stood on the mountain top with the Governor who was now the new U.S. Congressman elected from the Eighth District of Central Louisiana.

The Bible says that, "When it rains, it rains on the just and the unjust alike," and that it is "appointed unto man once to die."

There was glory on that mountain top. For a few days I touched the face of God, believing justice had been done. Then from out of nowhere somehow an evil wind blew us off the pinnacle and into the valley.

The Governor's gone and I'm still walkin' the valley. . . A Louisiana Long Shot. . . moving forward.

Day 1
"Friday"

The Governor was breathing hard as he gave me orders to make the four thirty p.m. stump speaking in Wardville, a suburb of Pineville, across the river from Alexandria. As he barked his orders in that gruff and gravelly voice that sent millions to the polls to elect him Governor twice, I had a foreboding that all was not well.

"Don't forget," he said, "go on to the Vick Community and then to the eight p.m. speaking in Joyce." Joyce was right outside of Winnfield, the parish seat of Winn, his beloved home parish. "I'll be right behind you," he added. He never showed up and he never went to his Winnfield birthplace alive again.

When I left the Bentley Hotel in downtown Alexandria to head for the first speaking in Wardville, the sun was shining brightly, the sky was a crystal blue. A few white clouds drifted slowly and lazily in the far distant heavens. Tomorrow was Election Day. Win, lose or draw, it would be over. As the Governor said, "We had done our dead-level best." And we figured on winning. Still, why was there a queasy feeling in my stomach? I'd followed this routine a hundred times, a lonely guitar picker, a singer of songs, a singer of "The Ballad of Earl K. Long." My job was to sing and introduce the various speakers before the Governor spoke. Hadn't he called me, 'The Po' Man's Jimmie Davis,' because all he could afford was one guitar and one singer, as opposed to Jimmie Davis' Big Nashville/Hollywood entourage?

It seems like the sun has always shined the brightest when the worst was going to happen in my life. How was I to know that in just seven hours, the Governor would embark on an eleven dark day journey to glory? As I crossed the muddy Red River on a bridge where a sign said, "Built under the administration of Governor O.K. Allen," the queasy feeling was beginning to disappear. I prepared in my mind to wind up these last three speakings. Little was I to know that the star of the show would never appear.

As I stepped up to the microphone on the back of the pickup truck in Wardville, anxious faces looked up at me; I was just a prelude for the excitement to come. I whipped out a rockabilly rhythm to "Kansas City," while my mind went racing forward trying to figure when to sing the old Baptist hymn that Uncle Earl loved so well, "In the Garden." There was a restlessness in the crowd as I sang my number one hit, for the star of the show was still absent. As I concluded my act, I introduced the Governor's esteemed attorney, Joe Arthur Sims, of Hammond, the man who helped rescue the Governor from the evil clutches of two mental institutions, I had no reason to believe that the Governor would not appear. Joe Arthur took the mike, and with a booming voice said, "Thank you, Jay." Then proceeded to expound on the virtues of Earl K. Long and what the Longs' had done for Louisiana.

"Ladies and Gentlemen," his big oratorical voice resounded, as I got in my car to go to the next speaking. "There would be no free school lunches for our hungry little children, had it not been for Earl K. Long. There would be no free school books, no old age pensions." His voice trailed off as I sped down the road to the next speaking at Vick.

When Joe Arthur got to Vick, he told me Earl had not shown up for the speaking in Wardville when he left. This was not unusual as Uncle Earl was always late. I was told to go on to Joyce, about fifty miles north of Alexandria in Winn Parish. Joe Arthur said he would meet me there. I repeated the same scene in Vick and with a tired numbness in my mind, I thought, the campaign would soon be over with one more speaking. Leaving Vick, the restless foreboding I had felt earlier, crept back into my spirit. Somewhere, I had a pint of whiskey. Maybe a good slug was what I needed. I stopped at a little country store and bought a Coke chaser. The whiskey burned going down my throat, but it took my mind off the campaign for a while as I drove into the summer twilight heading for Winn Parish.

I stepped upon the back of the pickup truck in Joyce and looked out over the crowd. It was then I saw one of our campaign cars wheel up to the back of the crowd and come to a jerking halt. Out jumped Ellis "Easy Money" Littleton. He was out of breath as he pushed his way through the crowd and then tugged at my pants' leg. I leaned over to hear what he had to say and my worst fears became a reality.

"You've got to get back to the Bentley right now. They think Earl has had a heart attack," he breathlessly whispered in my ear.

"Are you sure?" I exclaimed in a loud whisper.

"Well, sure as I can be. Dr. Parrott is with him and they want you back right away."

"Damn it, Easy Money, don't let anyone here know what you just told me or we'll lose the election for sure," I cried in a hoarse, half-frightened whisper. Dr. Parrot was family, he was married to Earl's sister's daughter.

The microphone stand seemed to reel in my grasp as I said, "Ladies and Gentlemen, there's been a change in plans. Due to last minute campaign pressures, the Governor could not make it to this last speaking. However, he wanted me to give you his best wishes and to sing for you. Afterwards, we'll have some free bags of groceries and ice cold drinks for the kids and any adults that want them too. The Governor appreciates your support. Now here's my number one hit, "The Ballad of Earl K. Long."

My mind was racing a thousand miles an hour as I ended the toughest singing assignment of my young, professional career. The speedometer needle had just passed the one hundred miles per hour mark on the new Buick I was driving when the dead-end stop sign loomed up a hundred yards ahead on Highway Seventy-One.

"Damn it!" I'd forgot about this dead-end turn on Highway Eighty-Four as the Buick fishtailed and spun one hundred eighty degrees. The back bumper clipped the stop sign and the sign was still swaying as I straightened the car and headed for

Alexandria on Highway 167 south.

I looked at my watch. It was eight forty-five p.m. The moonlight gleamed on the half-empty whiskey bottle on the front seat next to me. It had slid out from under the seat during my almost fatal crash. Now, I felt like I really needed a long drink to steady my nerves. Fifteen minutes later, the whiskey still felt warm on my stomach, as I sped through the moonlit night, for I had no time to stop for a Coke chaser. Uncle Earl was in trouble, big trouble, if what Easy Money had told me was true.

"Damn it! How could a pretty sunshiny day turn into such a horrible night?" The virgin pine timber that lined each side of the highway looked like giant Christmas trees silhouetted by the rising moonlight. "Hell, there'd be no Christmas for us if we didn't win the election and if Earl does have a heart attack, what in the world will we tell the press?" These were my thoughts racing through my mind like a Gulf coast hurricane, trying to destroy everything we'd been working so hard for these last three months. It was nine-fifteen p.m. In forty-five minutes, I would have an answer. It would come from Uncle Earl, the master himself.

As I pushed the button on the elevator in the lobby of the Bentley Hotel, it seemed like an eternity before the doors opened. As I glanced around the empty lobby, I wondered where all the press was. Suddenly, the door opened and I stepped inside. When the doors reopened, I had my answer. The hallway leading to Uncle Earl's room was full of press people, gawkers, would-be newshounds and probably even spies from the enemy camp. There was a blur of faces. It felt like a crowd of two hundred. How could so many people be in such a narrow hallway? Finally, I recognized two familiar faces, Jim McLain of the Associated Press and Jerry Moses of the United Press.

"Jay, how's the Governor? What's going on? Did he make any of his speakings? Did he have a heart attack?"

"I don't know, men. That's what I aim to find out, as soon as you let me by," I stated rather abruptly.

"Make way, make a hole, let Jay through," someone shouted. I knocked loudly on the door. I knew we were in a political life or death situation for sure. My knees felt like rubber and my heart was still racing.

"Who is it?"

"Jay," I shouted through the din of voices in the hallway. The door cracked open and as I slid inside, my worst fears were realized.

There lay the Governor unmoving under a huge oxygen tent that covered over three-quarters of his bed. There were two oxygen tanks standing in the corner of the room at the head of his bed with air hoses leading to the tent. At the foot of his bed stood Dr. Parrott, with a long curved pipe in his mouth. He looked like Sherlock Holmes. Someone had done a damn good job of making our hotel room look like the third floor of the big Baptist Hospital down the street. There were a couple of blurred faces on the opposite side of the Governor's bed.

"How is he, Dr. Parrott?" I breathlessly inquired in a barely audible whisper.

"I'm afraid he's had a serious heart attack by all indications," he replied.

"Are you sure?" I snapped.

"Well, not one hundred percent, but whatever it is, he needs to be in the hospital, but he refuses to move from here," he stated emphatically.

"Who's that?" the Governor hoarsely muttered from under the oxygen tent.

"It's me, Jay," I replied excitedly, responding to the movement and sound of my only Commander-in-Chief's voice.

"Well, what took you so long? How did the speakings go? Were there many people?" Three rapid fire questions disturbed the doctor, but got my adrenaline flowin' like the wind.

"Well, I drove a hundred miles an hour to get here, as soon as Easy Money told me. The speakings were great. There was a lot of people there and they all said, you were gonna win.

"Hell, I know that," he said. "What else?" he snapped. The moment of truth was at hand.

"Governor, there's more press people in the hallway than I've ever seen in my life. Every newspaper and TV camera in the state is here, plus UPI and Associated Press! What are we going to do. . . I mean, tell them," I blurted out disregarding Dr. Parrott's stern looks.

"I'll tell you what we're going to do. Get this God damn tent off me. Get a comb and comb my hair, prop me up in this bed, and we're gonna give 'em the damnedest five-minute interview you've ever seen," said the Governor as he started clawing at the oxygen tent.

"Please, Governor, calm down, relax. You can't see anybody," exclaimed Dr. Parrott.

"The hell, I can't. Do as I say, Jay, or you are all fired, every last one of you. Nobody's gonna tell Uncle Earl what to do!"

"Yes sir," I cried with glee. By God, this sounded like the Earl Long I knew; at least we'd die with our boots on! As we folded back the oxygen tent and I started to comb his hair and straighten his pajamas, he started giving orders like a General.

"Tell Jerry Moses and Jim McLain, I'll give them a five-minute interview on one condition. That is. . . they break the story to the rest of the press. If they don't agree to that, they can go straight to hell, a wonderin' what's going on. You got that?"

"Yes sir!"

"Well, God damn it, see that you say it just like I told you."

"Yes sir, I will. Don't worry about that," I said as I nearly stumbled over Dr. Parrott heading for the door.

Opening the door against the pressing flesh of the crowd outside proved to be quite a chore itself, but I had a fresh second wind and a new strength surging through my body. As I struggled to get back into the hallway, I sensed that the Governor had once again put us in control. His political genius, mental and physical stamina never ceased to astound me. I felt a fleeting victory now back in our grasp. This new-found courage made me shout for quiet in the hallway. As I raised my hands and called for attention, I heard the murmur of voices rippling through the crowd for everyone to shut up and listen to what I had to say. Even without a microphone, I felt in control and in command of center stage.

"All right, listen up," I exclaimed in my most authoritative former Marine Buck Sergeant voice.

"The Governor is doing fine and has agreed to an interview on two conditions," I carefully stated as I let the sound of this statement sink in.

"What is it?" someone shouted.

"First of all, only Jim McLain and Jerry Moses are allowed to come in the room and for only five minutes and secondly, Jim, you and Jerry have to break the story to the rest of the press here. Is that agreeable to everyone?" I shouted.

"You bet," came a unanimous chorus of voices. Jerry and Jim nodded in agreement. I went over the rules one more time, emphasizing the five-minutes-only rule with Jerry and Jim before we squeezed our way back into the room.

The Governor propped up with two pillows behind his back, looked like a million dollars, even if he was a little peaked around the eyes.

"How you feeling, Governor?" said Jim McLain.

"Fine, fine," he exclaimed.

"What's wrong with you, Governor? Some say a heart attack," queried Jerry Moses.

"Nah, boys, just a little touch of ptomaine poisoning, I guess," the Governor replied. "I sent Jay over to Shorty's Barbecue to get me some of those good pork sandwiches, and they must have been a little over-ripe and upset my stomach. At my age, it don't take much, you know," he replied to both Jerry and Jim. Five minutes went by awfully fast, as they turned to the Doctor who nodded affirmation to every little lie the Governor was telling. Well, it wasn't all lies. I did go get those barbecue pork sandwiches earlier in the day for him and they didn't taste so good after all. As I escorted Jerry and Jim to the door, sweat was dripping from under my arms and I wondered how the Governor could look so calm. As I closed the door behind Jim and Jerry, the doctor was already pulling the oxygen tent back over the Governor's upper torso. His eyes were closed and he was soon snoozing, dreaming of victory, I hoped. Tonight, we looked hell straight in the eye and made the damn devil blink!

Day II
"Saturday"

It was a great day for an election! The sun was shining. That meant that everybody could go to the polls. The money that I'd delivered to the different sheriffs to have voters hauled to the polls should have been well-spent, if the son-of-bitches didn't pocket it all! I needed to work the phones, but I was really afraid to leave the Governor's side. He had a pretty peaceful night, and now he was sedated, but still restless.

"Did you get all that money to Sheriff Craft in Leesville?" he stirred under the oxygen tent and listened for my reply.

"Yes sir, and I told him to make sure someone was a haulin' voters to that Evans' box," I replied.

"How many votes in that box?" he asked.

"Ninety-two, and they're all voting for you!" I rhymed.

"How you know?" he queried.

"'Cause it's a little old country box, and we put on a good show and you spoke very well out there," I stated. "Besides, they all like Country music, hymns and the free bags of groceries you gave them," I added.

"I wouldn't be so sure. I wouldn't count my chickens before they hatch," was his coarse but soft reply.

The Governor seemed a bit mellow today. I couldn't tell if it was the relaxing pills Dr. Parrott had given him, or if he was just at peace with himself, knowing that he had run a good race, fought a good fight and had kicked 'em in the ass. Maybe it was like all the races he had been in before, knowing that when you've done all that you can do, then it's up to the people to do the rest on election day. To him it was not a new experience. To me, I was drained like after a night of uninhibited sex. I was rather lethargic this Saturday morning, wanting to do something, but not knowing what to do.

We had twenty-four-thousand-plus dollars riding on a bet down at Charlie D'Amico's Sportsman Lounge. I guess I could go down and check with Charlie and maybe get a drink. I decided against this plan of action and chose to stay close to the Governor. I looked at my watch. It was ten a.m.

Hell, I can't even go vote, I thought. Well, I'll be damned, the Governor can't go vote either. Suppose we lose by two damn votes. That would be the crapoola of all time! Just our rotten-ass luck, I thought, as I tried to shake these fears from my mind. I saw Easy Money coming across the parking lot. I stepped outside to meet him.

"Hey Jay," he greeted, "How's Uncle Earl?"

"Fine," I replied. "You voted yet?" I asked.

"Hell no," he quipped.

"Why?" I exclaimed.

"Ain't registered."

"Well, I'll be damned, man, why not?" I stated furiously.

"Hell, I can't read nor write," he said sheepishly.

"Son-of-a-bitch," I muttered, embarrassed. I had forgotten Easy Money had only a third grade education. The only thing he could do well was drive and punch cattle, plus put up signs and other little odds and ends the Governor would have him do. There must have been a hundred Easy Money's that the Governor gave odd jobs to. He always looked out for the underprivileged, orphans, widows, and the poor whites and blacks.

"Hell's bells, we've just got to win this election," I exclaimed half-out loud.

"We will," was Easy's reply.

"How you know?" I retorted.

"This is the Eighth District. It's made up of country folks and they ain't never let him down. They're proud of him, no matter what. He's one of them and it's hard to go against your own kind," Easy Money stated simply and philosophically.

Hell, I wish I could be that sure, I thought. Didn't make sense to me, cause I'll be damned if they didn't crucify Jesus in his own home town. Nope, if we win this election, it'll be because we worked day and night, living off of two, three or four hours sleep a night. It had almost killed me, and I was twenty-four years old. The Governor was sixty-four and had out-worked all our asses. He had called in all his green stamps, plus we had spent a lot of that all-mighty green stuff with George Washington's picture on it.

"Easy, why don't you monitor some of the voting booths for the rest of the day and report back to us tonight," I stated.

"What you gonna do?" he replied.

"Stay close to the Governor and make sure no reporters get close to him, or worse than that, make sure no one tries to kill him before eight p.m.," was my reply.

"Sounds like a winner to me," Easy said, as he turned to walk away. "See ya when the polls close," he saluted farewell.

Four p.m. and four hours to go before the polls close. I wondered what in the world Easy Money was finding out. I was no longer lethargic. The tension was beginning to build in every fiber of my body. The anticipation was worse than a bridegroom's on his wedding day. I wondered if it was the same for a virgin on her wedding night. Nevertheless, it was both heaven and hell at the same time. The Governor had wanted to make some phone calls, and I was trying to monitor the time spent with each call, so that he wouldn't wear himself out. I still wasn't sure whether he'd had a heart attack or not. Dr. Parrott had given strict orders for him to remain quiet. He would have a coronary himself if he knew the Governor was still calling ward bosses after he left.

"Turn the TV on. Let's see what the six o'clock news reporters have to say," his gravelly command brought me back to reality. As I looked at my watch, it was six p.m. straight up and down. The old black and white set would stay on till ten p.m. By then, we'd know the outcome of the race, and we could move the Governor, as previously planned, on to the Baptist Hospital up the street. The polls would have been closed for two hours, and the die cast one way or the other.

The announcer said it looked like a heavy turnout. He went on to give the news, the weather report, and to speculate on the excitement of the Eighth District's last hurrah for Governor Earl K. Long. The Governor trailed by approximately five thousand votes in the first primary, and no one expected him to win in the second. No one that is, except for the Governor himself. Charlie D'Amico was nervous about the bet. If the Governor was worried, he damn sure didn't show it now or when he let the bet ride. Matter-of-fact, I never even heard him mention the bet anymore, until after the second primary.

We were alone for this election night in more ways than one. Practically all of the old political cronies had jumped ship. One had even tried to shake the Governor down for thirty thousand dollars. When the Governor wouldn't shake, he went to the other side taking with him tales of some of the Governor's escapades both real and imagined. The Governor had sent his lady friend, Blaze, back to Maryland for the duration of the campaign three months earlier, so they couldn't throw that up in his face. He and Blaze prearranged all of this, and they had gotten the jump on some of his political enemies.

The worst they could say about him now was that he was crazy, because he had been committed to two mental institutions by his estranged wife Blanche and nephew, Russell Long, who was a U.S. Senator. But he rebutted that out on the political trial by saying, "If I'm crazy now, I was crazy then, and some of you must be crazy too, because you voted for me three or four times!" This would always get a big laugh, and I believed it would help him get elected on this Saturday night, because he faced the issue head on, just like he faced everything else in life. I believed the people sensed the truth in this statement, and his statement that he had been framed by some of his over-anxious friends. A great writer once said, "With every adversity, there is a seed of equal and equivalent benefit. All you have to do is look for it!" The Governor sure epitomized this statement to the great chagrin of his political enemies.

It was eight p.m. and the polls were closed. God help us, I thought silently. And then a silent prayer went through my mind. If it be your will, dear God, please let us win this election. Eight thirty p.m. The tallies were coming in. We had a horse race, neck and neck, with the city votes coming in first. As the nine o'clock hour approached, some of the country boxes began trickling in, and the Governor started edging ahead. Then the announcer called out, "Evans, Louisiana. . . ninety-one votes for Earl K. Long, and one vote for Harold B. McSween."

"How many votes in that Evans' box, Jay?" growled the Governor.

"Ninety-two, sir," I replied.

"Who you reckon that son-of-a-bitch was that didn't vote for me out there?" he went on.

"I don't know, and it don't make any difference, cause you're a fixin' to whip their ass good," I hollered back. It was now nine thirty p.m. and we were a thousand votes ahead with only country boxes left to count. Damn it, Easy Money was right. By God, they weren't going to crucify Earl in the Eighth District. No sir, not by a long shot, not tonight. We were bound for glory and Washington, D.C.

"Congressman Long. . . uh. . . I mean, Governor, Dr. Parrott's here. We've got an ambulance to take you over to the Baptist Hospital," I stated with as much nervous anticipation as I could muster, fully expecting a verbal tongue lashing and reprimand.

"What time is it?" the Governor said.

"Ten o'clock," I replied.

"How far ahead are we?" he asked.

"Twenty-five hundred votes. There's no way for him to catch you now," I stated.

"We need five thousand to win the God damn bet with Glenn Lowe," he mumbled.

"You'll get it," I affirmed rather shakily. "There's nothing, but country boxes left and you're carrying them all by a wide majority," I exclaimed. "Let's go on to the hosiptal where you can get some rest before the reporters come a swarmin' up here for an interview," I went on. I startled him with that statement, and he calmly agreed to go on to the Baptist Hospital.

Yep, rest and relaxation was what we all needed now. A modern hospital room did-n't sound so bad after all. I was already planning ways to secure the perimeter and keep all intruders out, including former and present enemies. There were a lot of snakes that would come crawling back, and maybe even some who might have assas-sination on their minds. It was a new ball game. It called for a new defense. I was in strange territory. The Baptist Hospital sounded like the safest place to be.

Day III
"Sunday"

The Sunday morning papers told the news in a bold heading: The man who called himself, "The Last of the Red Hot Papas," couldn't have been happier. Those who had counted him out for good were licking their new wounds and looking for a place to hide. I imagined there were a powerful lot of uneasy people this Sunday morning who had wished old Uncle Earl would have succumbed to the ptomaine poison he was reported to have had this past Friday night. Yes sir, Uncle Earl was back in the saddle again, and I was right there with him. Damn, it felt good to win! I hadn't felt this good since my record had gone "number one" a year ago this month, and Jimmy Stretch had sent word in the middle of the night for me to hightail it to Baton Rouge for interviews. Shoot, Baton Rouge wouldn't even hold a candle to Washington, D.C. I wondered in my mind how Washington society would tolerate old Uncle Earl. Huey had set the Senate on its collective ear by brazenly smoking a cigar in the U.S. Senate chamber. I wondered what Earl would do to get attention. Uncle Earl would probably split a watermelon wide-open with his Case pocketknife and offer everybody a piece on the floor of the House, or worse yet, he just might spit on the floor. Whatever it would be, God knows, they'll know we're there. Washington won't be the same. The Eighth District won't ever be the same! Russell and Blanche damn sure won't have an easy moment never knowing what's going to happen next. Hell, I wonder if he'll squire Blaze around Washington the way he did in New Orleans? These thoughts kept running through my head as I called friends to report the news. I answered the phone most of the day while Earl rested.

"Doctor's orders," I told everyone. "He cannot speak on the phone. He needs total bed rest for a few days." Former President Truman called to give his regards and congratulations. I thanked him and wished him well, along with a call from Senator Lyndon Johnson of Texas and other dignitaries from across the state and nation. They were all understanding as to why they couldn't talk to the new Congressman and each had kind things to say on the phone about him.

It was strange calling the Governor, Congressman. It didn't sound right, and I made up my mind for the time being just to keep on addressing him as Governor or Uncle Earl. He seemed to like that. He was heavily sedated and resting now as I went through the telegrams and other congratulatory messages we had received. God, it felt good to win! It was a hell of a lot better feeling than last December when we lost in the first primary to Chep Morrison and Jimmie Davis. I could still feel the lump in my throat at the thought of losing. It was the same feeling I had in Meridian, Mississippi when I lost the Jimmie Rodgers Country Music Festival Contest by one point to come in second place nationwide. When you don't win first place, it feels like you've been kicked in the stomach by a Missouri mule. Close only counts in horseshoes and hand grenades and don't mean crap in horse races or politics when you've got it all bet on first place.

It was the best Sunday in my life and I was going to savor every moment of this day. Tomorrow was Monday, the beginning of a new work week. Tomorrow I'd ask the Governor what we were going to do in the halls of Congress to make them notice us. It was hard to believe he was now a freshman Congressman. It didn't sound right somehow, not at his age. In a few days, he'd be sixty-five, and he already had more political and governing experience than half of all the people in D.C. combined. You can bet your last dollar to a doughnut hole that I'll never call him a freshman Congressman. He'll always be the Governor to me. Sounds more important anyway!

Day IV
"Monday"

Monday morning! I couldn't believe my eyes! There was the Governor in a straight back chair at the foot of his hospital bed, getting a shave and haircut. I was guarding the door and looking on in amazement. For a man who three days earlier was supposed to have had a heart attack, he looked might darn chirpy to me! Damn, he just looked good! He looked like a winner. He was asking the barber all sorts of questions about his family, his garden, his children and so forth. About that time, there was a gentle knock on the door. I stepped outside. Charlie D'Amico and Bob Levins from Rapides Bank were standing in the hall. Charlie had a brown paper sack in his hand.

"How's Uncle Earl this morning?" they inquired.

"Fine," I said. "He's getting a haircut," I stated. With a bewildered and relieved look on their faces, they both laughed.

"Jay, he called earlier this morning and wanted me to deliver this package. Can we come in?" Charlie asked.

"You bet," I replied. I had an idea what was in the sack.

"Come in, come in, boys. What's going on?" Uncle Earl asked of the two unwitting cohorts.

"Everything's good, Governor. How about yourself?" replied Charlie.

"Couldn't be better, couldn't be better. How's everything at the bank, Bob?" Uncle Earl asked.

"Fine, governor," Bob stated. "I must say you're looking good," he went on.

"I feel good. I always feel good after a shave and haircut. Charlie, did you bring what I told you?" he asked.

"Sure did, Governor, right here in this paper sack," Charlie replied.

"Dump it out on the foot of the bed," the Governor said as he climbed back in bed and propped up against his raised hospital bed and pillows.

As Charlie dumped the contents of the paper bag on the foot of the Govenor's bed, the barber and Bob Levins' eyes widened in surprise. Tumbling out of the brown bag were fives, tens, twenties and hundred dollar bills. The Glenn Lowe bet now belonged to the Governor. All of it. "Count it, Jay," the Governor stated matter-of-factly, as he gleefully looked on. I began to count, arranging the bills in thousand dollar stacks.

After what seemed an eternity, I declared, "Twenty-four thousand, four hundred and eighty dollars right on the nose."

"Humph," said Earl. "Count it again, Jay," he went on. I was faster this time.

"Twenty-four thousand, four hundred eighty dollars to the dollar," I said. The odd numbers reflected some small bets Charlie had been holding for the Governor.

"Bob, you take the money, put it back in that sack, and take it on down to the bank for me," declared Earl.

"Yes sir, Governor," Bob replied. Charlie looked relieved as they all said good day and that they would see the Governor again soon and wished him well. That was the last time either Earl or I saw the money!

Day V
"Tuesday"

I woke up thinking about the money Uncle Earl had won the day before. Little did I know it would be the last bet he would ever make. He bet on himself, a true long shot! He won! That was great, I thought. Now, a few of the snakes were trying to crawl back. Mrs. Blanche had called, inquiring about the Governor and wanting to know if she come up for the weekend. Dick Davis had been snooping around. Otherwise, all was quiet on this Tuesday morning. The Eighth District was settling down rather nicely, I thought, probably comfortable with the thought that another Long had been elected. All was well in Louisiana, even though some thought this one was crazy. What the hell, weren't all politicians a little touched in the head? The Longs were maybe more than most. For what would make a man or woman for that matter, want to forsake all to serve others? It didn't make sense. I believe it's the race itself that makes politicians run. . . the excitement, the gamble, the not-knowing and the winner take-all atmosphere. It's a lot like an illicit love affair, where if you're caught, you lose, unless you can make the public believe in you, not your lying eyes.

Whatever the case may have been. . . It was a mundane Tuesday. I questioned the nurse about the pills she was bringing the Governor to take three times a day. I began to wonder about protecting the new Congressman, as I carried a .38 Smith & Wesson Special everywhere I went now. However, this would be no protection at all if someone wanted to poison his food or slip him a poison pill. I examined all of his food, and therefore deemed it appropriate to inquire about the little white pills and the one long dark brown capsule.

"I don't know what they're for," stated the nurse. "You'll have to ask Dr. Parrott. He prescribed them," she went on evasively.

"Well, I'll do just that, when the doctor comes around this evening," I said.

Later that evening, I cornered Dr. Parrott in the hall, out of ear shot of the Governor. "Dr. Parrott," I said in my best salesman like voice, "could you describe the function of each of the pills you have prescribed for the Governor?"

"Why certainly," Dr. Parrott replied, pumping up his chest with pride. "One is for the heart, one is to relax, and one is for his kidneys."

"And how about the long brown capsule," I coaxed.

"Oh, that is to keep the fluid down in his lungs, and to keep him from coughing, so as not to put a strain on his already overworked heart," he declared.

"Thank you, Doc. I just wanted to know, because you can't be too careful these days," I added.

"That's right, Jay. Just ask me, anytime," he stated. Somehow, this set my mind at ease. After all, he was a doctor and related to Uncle Earl by marriage. It would be ludicrous to believe that the doctor or anyone in the hospital would try to hurt good ole Uncle Earl. Still, there was a stirring in my soul, even if ever so faintly. I passed it off an an overly active imagination and settled in for the night.

Day VI
"Wednesday"

Today, my wife came to see me. She's pregnant with our second child. If it's a boy, maybe I'll name him after Uncle Earl. "How's the Governor?" she said, as we kissed, "and how are you? God, we've missed you, and you haven't been home in over two weeks. Your mother and father are worried about you. They're afraid you might get killed," she blurted out.

"Baby, don't worry about me," I said. "The Governor's fine and everything's going to be all right. Tell Mom and Dad not to worry," I added.

"Are you going to Wasington with him?" she questioned apprehensively.

"We'll talk about it later," I replied.

"Jan misses you and wants her daddy to come home," she stated.

Damn, she had hit a nerve there, for Jan was my little daughter, our first child, and I loved her with all my heart. I hadn't seen much of her in the last three months, even though sometimes I was as close as ten miles from home, but I couldn't leave the Governor alone at night. He was paranoid and afraid that someone was trying to kill him.

Some nights, I even slept at the foot of his bed in the motel rooms on a day bed, blocking the door, in case someone tried to break in. This had happened to him before in New Orleans, when he was in a room with Blaze. Some thugs with a huge railroad crosstie had broken the door down. Outside, Mrs. Blanche was standing, giving orders and telling the Governor he had shamed her for the last time. This made a lasting impression on the Governor, and for that reason, he didn't want it to happen again. I don't blame him; I would have been paranoid too. If a son-of-a-bitch broke in on us now, he'd face six ways of dying from a .38 Special. I had made up my mind to shoot first and ask questions later.

"Tell Jan I love her, and I will see her soon," I whispered. "Honey, we don't have to make a decision on Washington until January, and that's four months away. Now you had better run along. You must be tired of being pregnant like that. When is the baby due, anyway?" I asked playfully.

"The doctor says anytime this month. If you all stay up here much longer, I'll just get a room right next to Earl's, so you can watch out after the both of us. It'll probably be the only way I'll get to see you anyhow. Sometimes, I think you love the Governor more than me, Jan, your mom and dad, plus your horses and your old squirrel dog, Spotty," she said.

"You know better than that," I stated half-heartedly. No doubt about it, I was caught up in the Governor's web. It was hard to separate my life and wants from his. I had been bitten by the political bug, and I would pay the price dearly in the years to come. I didn't know this now, nor did I want to know the future, as I kissed my wife goodbye and walked her down the hall to the elevator.

Day VII
"Thursday"

The Governor was looking better. Evidently, Dr. Parrott's medicine was doing the trick. I had stocked the closet inside his hospital room with vodka, Seagram's VO, Scotch, wine and his favorite bourbon whiskey, Old Forester. However, he didn't call for a drink or anything special, just cornbread, buttermilk, mustard greens and field peas with rice. From time to time, he had fiddled with the new will he had folded lengthwise inside of his coat pocket hanging in the closet. I had his old silver aluminum suitcase stuck down in the bottom of the closet with extra pajamas, underwear and clean white shirts. We had several suits of clothing here in the hospital plus all of our traveling clothes at the Bentley Hotel, just three blocks away. We could have moved at a moment's notice and been ready to travel. We had two brand new Ford station wagons plus the yellow Dodge station wagon that he had bought for Blaze and Polly Cavanaugh. We also had a brand new Buick LeSabre. We could have made our getaway in style at anytime day or night. Somehow though, I felt it would be a long time before we would be leaving the Baptist Hospital. My wife could very well be right. She would probably wind up with a room next to Earl's before it was all over.

I had time on my hands to daydream about Washington in between rubbing the Governor's legs with Jergens lotion and trying to keep him abreast of the news. Sometimes, his legs would cramp so bad he would grimace in pain. I would rub all the harder, just as the doctor had ordered and wished that we were out at Hot Wells, where he could get a good professional massage.

Day VIII
"Friday"

Thursday came and went uneventfully. Today was Friday and Friday represents pay day. Money burns a hole in a Southern boy's pocket. Well, this Southern boy wasn't going anywhere today, and there damn sure wasn't any money in my pockets. I was still betting on the next roll of the dice.

God, it didn't seem like a week ago today, Uncle Earl had his heart attack. I still didn't know whether he had a heart attack or not. I was carefully checking his pills every day to make sure nothing changed. The doctor was cautiously optimistic about his prognosis and Earl's progress. I think half the time they just guessed anyhow.

The Governor looked all right to me. Every day he seemed to be getting stronger and stronger. I thought, God, this is the toughest old bird I have ever seen. Hell, he'll never die. He'll outlive all of us and his enemies, too. I really believed he was indestructible. I knew that no one could outlast, outfox, outsmart or out-politic the old man. He was literally my hero, and even more so since last Friday.

Reflecting on the events of the past week, I had never before seen anyone with as much political, mental, or physical courage as Earl K. Long. He was the best psychological poker player I had ever seen. One thing for sure, when God made Uncle Earl, he threw away the mold. As far as I was concerned, he was "The Last of the Red Hot Papas" in more ways than one. Hell, it took a lot of guts to stay holed up in that hotel room from two thirty p.m. on a Friday afternoon until ten p.m. Saturday on election night, especially with the doctor telling him, "You've had a heart attack and need to be moved to the hospital." He knew how to play the odds. If they moved him, he would certainly have lost the election, and if he had died it wouldn't have made a darn bit of difference. If he stayed, he might have died before the polls closed, and it still wouldn't make any difference. If he lived, he had a chance of winning. Then if he had won and died, he would have gone out in a blaze of glory, a winner! By God, there is no substitute for winning. He played the odds. . . a long shot. He won. He must have been suffering a lot of physical and mental pain with a heart attack at the worst possible moment. I wondered if I could have made those decisions. I wondered how many other men could have. I sure didn't know any other politicians in this Governor's league.

Well, we won. We won because he won. I don't know why in the hell I'm sayin' we. There can only be one winner in a horse race or politics; I don't know, it just sounded right to say "We won" because I had stuck it out to the end, I guess. Somehow, I was caught up in his crusade. I couldn't differentiate between him and me. It seemed like now I was a physical extension of Earl K. Long. I wondered how many other people had been captured in this type of dilemma. Maybe it was my Marine Corps training to protect the Commander-in-Chief at all costs, even with my own life. To lay your body down over the grenade to protect your buddies, hadn't that been what they taught us in boot camp. I wondered if I could do that. In some way, the Governor's action last Friday and Saturday reminded me of that. He is brave, I thought. The soft moans from the bed startled me back from daydreaming. I knew his legs were hurting him as I reached for the lotion to give him a rub down.

Uncle Earl was a small man, not short, not tall, about five feet nine to five foot ten inches in height. He had said, "Hell, give me short people. They move faster, quicker and work harder. There's nothing no worse than a wet-ass fisherman or a fellow who smokes a pipe. They think too much, move too slow," he said. I guess he put all tall people in that category. Damn, Dr. Parrott smoked a pipe. I wonder what that means. I wonder if he fishes also.

I was reflecting on how shiny his legs were and how the blue varicose veins showed through the shine when he brought me suddenly back to reality with a gruff, "Have you seen Easy Money?"

"No sir, not today," I replied.

"You reckon he got those cows moved yet?" he queried half-heartedly.

"Yes sir, I believe so," was my reply. The cows he was talking about were some the Governor himself had purchased at Dominique's Livestock Auction Barn in Alexandria a few days before the end of the election. I darned sure couldn't forget those cows or how he bought them. We'd gone to the auction barn and had been there a little while when he suddenly remembered he had left an envelope with five thousand dollars in it between the mattresses of his bed at the Pea Patch farm.

"Jay, go back to the Pea Patch and bring me that envelope. Take the Buick," he commanded.

"Where's the envelope?" I replied.

"Hell, I don't know, just find it and bring it here," he shouted angrily.

"Yes sir," I replied as I headed for the door.

Son-of-a-bitch must think I'm a mind reader, I thought to myself half out loud as I sped down the highway to Winnfield. Wonder how fast this Buick will go? I thought. It's got one hundred twenty on the speedometer. Hell, I got that big black Mercury up to one hundred and ten on McArthur Drive when he was late for that speaking in Montgomery. I'll never forget that day, I thought. That was the day in Lecompte that he gave Dr. Scott a diamond-studded horseshoe ring. A few days later, he gave me one just like it. I proudly looked at it on my finger, gripping the Buick steering wheel and watched it glisten in the noonday sunlight. The speedometer was reading ninety miles per hour.

It took me two hours to go to the Pea Patch, find the envelope, and get back to the auction. It was a hundred miles round trip. When I walked inside the auction barn, Earl had a handful of sales tickets. He had bought forty-seven hundred dollars worth of cattle, about forty head in all. They were good cattle; I think maybe a cross between Charolais and Brahmas. Someone must have told him they were coming through the sale, or maybe he just wanted to create some excitement. I found out later that he used to own this auction barn and several more that he sold to old man Dominique.

He had given Easy Money some cash to fix the fences on his place, plus enough money to buy several rolls of wire and posts. He had told Easy Money to move those forty head of cattle down to his place on the river once he had it fixed up. I reckoned he was feeling pretty good, if he was asking about those old cows. I never heard of those cattle again, and Uncle Earl would never have the pleasure of seeing them being fattened up. The Governor was resting a little better now, and I went on out in the hall wondering about all the people holding things for the Governor.

I knew for sure the Governor had loaned Frank and Ruth Mathews some money to rebuild their King Lumber Company when their giant sawmill was destroyed by fire. Someone said that Earl had come to their rescue and loaned them three hundred thousand in cash. It must have been true, because they would send him cash money during his last campaign to help defray our mounting expenses. On one occasion, I signed for five thousand dollars in cash in a white envelope to be delivered to Uncle Earl. On another occasion, I just picked up a large brown envelope from the lumber company. Edgar Coco later told me there was fifty thousand dollars in it. I didn't open it, so I couldn't swear to that. For some reason, the Governor trusted me with large amounts of cash that I didn't even know I was carrying. If the old man died, there'd be a lot of rich people with their debts forgiven, I presumed. I guess being honest and not prying had paid off. Damn, we were on our way to Washington, D.C. I wondered, would I like D.C. as well as I liked New Orleans? I guess I'd know after the first year.

It was almost supper time and Friday was coming to a close. The nurse was bringing the little paper cup with the Governor's medicine. Guess I'd better check the pills. They were all there. Nothing was changed. All was well. Tomorrow would be Saturday.

Day IX
"Saturday"

The Baptist Hospital overlooks the Red River, butted up against a protecting levee. From the third floor, you could see the muddy waters of this once unpredictable river rush past, toward the Atchafalaya, on to the father-of-waters, and out to the Gulf of Mexico. Uncle Earl used to tell everyone on the stump speakings that central Louisiana was in the heart of the Red River Valley. He said many years ago, before the levees were built; the Red River would flood its banks in the springtime and bring all of the red mineral rich dirt from up in Oklahoma and northwest Texas down to God's country here in Louisiana. He said that after many years of flooding, this mineral-laced red dirt that made up the huge river plantations was as rich as the Nile Valley. He said you could grow anything in the world here. He was right. Some of the best cotton, cane, corn and soybeans in the world are grown right here in central Louisiana. He loved the farmers and farming, and they loved him.

It wouldn't be long before fall was here. Harvest time. Cotton-picking time. It was

Saturday, a day of rest? Not for the farmers, for in the fall they worked seven days a week 'til all the crops were in and the ground was laid by until spring plowing. Well, for us it would be just another day of rest. The Governor was getting stronger and stronger. I could feel a restlessness growing inside his mind, soul and body. It was ten a.m. The sun was shining brightly. Good for the farmers, I thought. I didn't know that in just four hours, all hell would break loose.

Two p.m. and I stepped out into the hall to catch a breath of fresh air. I heard the elevator doors click open and I saw trouble comin' up the hallway. "Damn it to hell, what's she doing here?" I whispered under my breath. I'll be a son-of-a-bitch, how am I going to handle this? I thought. They got closer. Yep, this was the hand-grenade, all right. Am I supposed to throw my body on it, mess in my pants or go blind? My mind was racing. My stomach had a knot in it and the electricity made my hair stand up on the back of my neck!

"Hello Jay, how's Earl?" Mrs. Blanche Long said. Hallway sunlight glinted off her perfectly coiffeured sandy red hair. Everything was just right about her. Every hair in place. Every pleat in her dress was just perfect.

"Fine, just fine, Miz Blanche, I stammered trying to regain my composure and wondering how to handle this ticking time bomb. The thought of killing her ran through my mind, but somehow that didn't seem the gentlemanly thing to do. She was cool as a cucumber and a matched set in anybody's league.

"Mrs. Hunt and I wondered if we could visit Earl for a few minutes," she calmly requested.

"Well, I. . .I. . . don't know. He's resting now and doctor's orders are no visitors at all, Miz Blanche," I stated, regaining some of my composure.

"It'll be all right for us to go in, Jay. I've already checked with Dr. Parrott and he said a brief visit would be okay," she went on as if I wasn't standing there. That pissed me off!

"That might be Dr. Parrott's orders, but I take my orders from the Governor, Ma'm."

"Well, ask him then. It'll only be for a moment," she persuaded. Hell, butter wouldn't melt in her mouth. For a moment, I swayed like the top of a big virgin pine tree in a soft summer breeze.

"Mrs. Hunt has to go on back home this evening, and she so wanted to see the Governor," she urged. Well, that did it. I guess I could ask the Governor. After all, his sister was with his estranged wife, so what harm could there be? In five minutes, I would regret that decision for the rest of my life.

"You wait right here, Miz Blanche. I'll be right back," I said as I eased into the Governor's room.

"What time is it?" the Governor said.

"Two fifteen," I replied.

"Uh. . . Governor, you've got some visitors outside," I stated as calmly as possible.

"Who is it?" he said, raising one questioning eyebrow.

"Your sister, Mrs. Hunt and your wife, Miz Blanche," I sputtered.

"What in the hell does she want?" he said with a scowl on his face.

"Miz Blance said she just wants to see how you are for a few minutes, and Mrs. Hunt, your sister was anxious to see you. She has to go back home to north Louisiana this afternoon. She said she had asked Dr. Parrott's permission and he said it was all right," I half-pleaded.

"Hell no! I don't want to see nobody, especially that old battle axe," he declared.

"Yes sir, but Governor she insists. After all it is your wife and maybe just for a minute then it would be all over with and they'll be gone," I pleaded. What a helluva predicament this was! I was wanting to get it over with in a hurry.

"Oh, all right, send them in," he conceded.

As I stepped back in the hall, I felt somehow relieved, but shaking inside. "Miz Blanche, the Governor will see you now, but only for a few minutes," I stated.

"Thank you, Jay," she said.

"I must warn you, if he becomes upset you'll have to leave immediately," I added.

"It'll be just a moment. We understand," she said and Mrs. Hunt nodded.

As they slipped through the door, I left it cracked so I could see and hear. Somehow, it didn't seem right to listen in on a man and his wife. Must have something to do with Southern chivalry or some crap like that.

"How you, Earl?" Blanche said, stepping over next to the bed.

"Oh, all right. What do you want?" the Governor retorted.

"Blanche was nice enough to give me a ride over here, Earl. You're looking well, are you eating all right?" Mrs. Hunt interjected quickly, half way in Blanches' defense and trying to diffuse the situation.

"Well, enough, sis," the Governor exclaimed grumpily. Earl's fuse was short, I could feel the fire racing towards the powder keg.

"How soon will you be getting out, Earl?" Blanche was trying for conversation.

"Soon enough," he snapped back.

"I thought maybe we could get together later on, talk and reconcile our differences when you are feeling better," she purred. Well, I'll be damned, the old bitch is wanting to be a Congressman's wife, I thought. Maybe, I won't go to D.C. after all.

"Reconcile? Reconcile hell! You son-of-a-bitch! Hell, no! You told them to strap me down like a tiger. You had 'em put me on that stretcher, stick them needles in my arms and in the boney part too! You told 'em the old bastard would be dead in a few days! Hell no, I ain't gonna reconcile, you bitch!" The Governor was shoutin' and sounded mad as hell. His face was livid, blue and white, and all kind of colors as I burst through the door to quickly usher out those two prim and proper Baptist Sunday School-looking ladies. Mrs. Hunt liked to have wet her pants and Blanche had an evil gleam in her eye. She looked like the cat who had eaten the canary as I quickly ordered both ladies out of the room. I rushed back in to try and calm down the still ranting and raving Earl K. Long.

"Who does that two-bit whore think she is? That no good son-of-a-bitch. Wouldn't help me when I was down. She turned everybody against me. Said I was crazy."

"Calm down, Governor. They're gone. She won't be back," I gasped.

"You damn right she won't be back. Not now or ever in my life. Rub my legs," he commanded.

"As I began to furiously rub his legs, the storm subsided just as quickly as it had arisen. I had never seen the Governor so mad for so long as I had known him. I just knew he was going to have a heart attack in the midst of it all. Hell, maybe that's what Blanche wanted. Maybe she wanted him to have a heart attack. It just didn't make sense. She ought to have known he would have reacted like this. Maybe she didn't know it. I was totally confused and somehow felt guilty for ever letting it happen. Somehow, I felt I had let the Governor down.

He was totally drained. He began to relax as I rubbed his legs with long, even strokes from his ankles all the way up to the knees. Maybe he needed to get it off of his chest. I knew one thing for sure, I'd never let Blanche Long within a hundred yards of the Governor again. His eyes were closing. Maybe, he would take a good nap before supper time. I looked at my watch. It was two thirty p.m.

As I stepped back into the hall, I could hear the Governor's deep breathing and occasional snoring. God, it was the best sound I had ever heard. I thought sure he was going to die, right on the spot in front of Mrs. Blanche and Mrs. Hunt. I still don't know how his heart survived all that strain. Damn, it liked to have killed me just listening. He must have the constitution of a horse! If that escapade didn't kill him, nothing will. Hell, he'll live forever, I thought to myself. By God in four months, he'll be as strong as ever. Look out D.C., here we come. Guitars, Governor and all! I wondered if they like Country music in Washington. Guess I'll find out soon enough.

Well, here comes the nurse right on time with the Governor's supper. My watch read five p.m. right on the button. Damn, this was a good hospital and efficient too. No hassles and the nurses were pleasant.

"You got the Governor's supper?" I said.

"Yep," she replied. "Meatloaf, mashed potatoes and gravy, snap beans, cornbread, buttermilk and Jell-O," she exclaimed teasingly.

"Hello, Jell-O. Every hospital in the world runs off Jell-O," I shot back with a smile.

"You bet, it's not fattening. How's the Governor?" she asked.

"Asleep," I replied.

"Good. I'll wake him," she winked. "Uncle Earl, Uncle Earl. I've brought your supper. Wake up now," the nurse coaxed.

"Hell, I am awake. I sleep with one eye open anyhow, in case something pretty or otherwise tries to slip up on me," he stated mischievously. All the rancor and the anger of the afternoon had completely faded away as if it had never happened.

"Now take your medicine, Governor, before supper," she chided.

"Hell, don't need no medicine. Medicine will make you sick. I feel fit as a fiddle. Just need some place to play," he grinned playfully.

"Well, I don't know about that, but doctor's orders are medicine before supper and again at bedtime," she ordered.

"Oh all right," the Governor said with mock disdain. "Where's the big capsule?" he inquired.

"This is all they gave me, sir. You must be getting better. This is what the doctor ordered," she replied.

As I went over to look at the pills, I noticed the big brown capsule was missing all right. At the time, it didn't seem strange, because the Governor was in such a good mood. Sometimes, no matter how close we look, we miss the red flags when they go up. There was a cold wind rippling across my soul, but I brushed it aside in the warmth of this moment.*

Day X
"Sunday"

The Catholic Church bells were ringing down the street, calling everyone to the ten o'clock mass at the beautiful St. Francis Xavier Catholic Cathedral. Kids were dressed up to go to Sunday School at the Emmanuel Baptist Church nearby and the Presbyterians were getting ready right across the street. There was something about Sunday morning church bells that was both comforting and lonesome. They are almost as lonesome as that old steam engine's whistle that used to blow for the Lecompte, Forest Hill/Midway crossing on the Red River and Gulf Railroad, as the train came abarreling through the piney woods late at night.

Yep, it was ten a.m. on a beautiful Sunday morning in Alexandria, Louisiana, USA, September, 1960. All was right in America. All was right with the Governor. Yes sir, Jay Chevalier had a lot to be thankful for this bright sunshiny Sunday morning. Little did I know that within twenty-four hours, I'd be the loneliest man in the world, with a broken heart as big as the crack of dawn that would never fully and completely mend!

"Those bells sound pretty. They're at the Catholic Church, I guess," the Governor said.

---

*Two seemingly innocent mistakes today, an estranged wife's visit and a missing pill. They would haunt me for the rest of my life. God forgive my youthful ignorance. The devil comes, but for to rob and steal in many disguises.

"Yes sir, I suppose. I ain't never been in no Catholic Church. . . my daddy would kick my ass. I was raised Baptist, reckon', I'll be one till the day I die," I retorted.

"Hell, Catholics are tolerant. If it hadn't been for them, I'd never finished my education at Loyola in New Orleans," he huffed. "Ain't no such thing as one right religion. All of 'em want to go to heaven. . . just usin' a different route, that's all. My mama was a rock-ribbed Baptist, but I guess I'm a little bit of everything. There's good in all those churches as well as bad." His voice seemed to trail off in philosophical thought.

Just as abruptly as he thought of religion, the Governor snapped back to the reality of the moment. "I want you to get that new Ford station wagon and put a single bed mattress down in the back of it," he blurted out.

"What for?" I exclaimed.

"Hell, we're breaking out of here Tuesday night. I've had about all this resting I can stand," he stated.

"Where are we going?" I questioned.

"To the Pea Patch. Get some clothes and head for west Texas for a two-week vacation. Maybe we'll go to Juarez, old Mexico, see the highlights and lowlights. Then, we'll come back here and stump the south for Kennedy," he reasoned.

"All right," I cried out. "I'll get everything ready."

Enough said. That was the end of the conversation. The Governor always left it up to me to figure out the details and execute the plan. I was all excited and scared at the same time. My mind was racing with thoughts both negative and positive. Stump the south for Kennedy? Damn, he's a Catholic. I thought the Governor wanted Senator Stuart Symington of Missouri to be President. Kennedy, huh? Well, he is a Democrat. I guess the Governor knows what he's doing. Wonder if he likes Country music. Hell that was the least of my worries. In his condition, suppose he drops dead while I'm taking him out of the hospital. Damn, I can't ask anyone to help me. I'll have to commandeer a wheelchair to take him downstairs. Wonder if I should tell Easy Money? On second thought, I ain't gonna tell anybody. They'd be an accomplice after the fact, and what the hell, he just may walk out. Whose gonna stop him? Well, it's Sunday. I'll worry about Tuesday later. After all, what did Scarlet O'Hara say, "Tuesday's just another day" or something like that. Jesus Christ, what am I going to do?

The nurse brought the Governor's pills and dinner in at twelve noon. He was in good spirits. The brown capsule was still missing, but no mention was made of the big, ugly son-of-a-gun. Hell, I wouldn't want to take that horse pill either. I still had no reason to believe anything was wrong. It was Sunday, and I was excited over the orders the Governor had just given me. The world was a great place to be on this Sunday in September. It was still warm, the sun was shining; almost warm enough to go swimming in Spring Creek. I don't know why that crossed my mind. I wondered where my cousin Pee Wee was. He lived on Spring Creek. Heck, he might be fishing. Wonder if he wants to go to Washington with me. I'll ask him later.

Sundays have a way of slipping by before you know it, then it's dark already. I wondered what they were doing at home in Forest Hill. Getting ready to eat supper, I reckon. Jan would say the blessing; dad would cut the cornbread, piling onions and Tabasco sauce onto his plate of field peas and rice. Mom had probably cooked fried chicken, and my wife was probably fixing the tea to be passed around the table, while she moved slowly, so as not to bump the soon-to-be new addition to our family. Yes sir, it couldn't have been a better Sunday. I really need to go home soon. It was only eighteen miles to Forest Hill. But it seemed like a thousand as I turned back to listen to the Governor talking on the phone.

"Well, you come up here tonight, you hear, and I'll talk to you then," he placed the phone abruptly back on the receiver and tried to gruffly hum an indistinguishable little tune. Sounded like "Bill Bailey" or "Goody, Goody."

"Who's that?" I asked.

"Easy Money. He's coming up later on tonight, so you can take off and go home for a while," he stated.

"Hell, I don't need to go home. Besides, I'm afraid to leave you here by yourself," I stated emphatically.

"Won't be by myself. Easy'll be here," he said. I knew there was no use to argue now. I'd tend to it later. Somehow and from somewhere I felt a deathly chill pass over the back of my neck. Must be the sun going down. The September night was coming on fast, causing a dampness to fill the evening air that seemed unusual for this time of year. There was supposed to be an eclipse of the moon tonight. The city lights were flickering on across town, and people were settling in for the night. Jim Bowie had walked these same streets over one hundred twenty-five years ago. Heroes of a different time, but in the same place as we were now, I thought. I wondered what the town looked like in the early 1800s.

Uncle Earl was a hero, maybe not like Bowie, but a hero just the same. Hell, heroes put their breeches on just like everybody else, one pant leg at a time, I thought to myself. You bet your ass. Heroes are just ordinary men who rise to extraordinary occasions, I reasoned to myself. I wondered if the Presbyterians were right about the predestination stuff in the Bible. I wonder if God knows who's going to be heroes or not. Hell, if it's predestinated, and God knows it, that just blows my theory all to hell about ordinary men and extraordinary occasions. Still, I believed the Governor was a hero. I don't know whether it was preordained or it just happened; maybe you got to die to be a hero. Hell, they shot Huey, Lincoln and Garfield. Maybe you gotta get shot to be a hero. Damn it to Hell, the Governor's a living hero, at least to me he is, I pondered. I don't believe anybody believes you're gonna be a hero, least of all yourself. I believe heroes just happen. They kind of evolve. Nobody plans to be a hero.

The price is too damn high! Don't guess anyone will know the Governor's a hero but me, because if you have to die to be a hero, he's too tough to die. Hell, after what he's been through, he'll live forever or at least to be a hundred. What the hell, the mind sure plays funny tricks on you. Don't know why I'm thinkin' this kind of crap anyway. Think I'll go and get a Sunday paper.

"Earl and Blanche Long have reconciliation talk at the Baptist Hospital Saturday afternoon." The sentence blared out at me from the pages of the paper and numbed my mind. Hell's Bells, son-of-a-bitch! If the Governor sees this, he'll go crazy for sure, I thought. Probably have another heart attack on the spot, I visualized. Who in the hell drummed up this phony ass story, I wondered. Hadn't he told her yesterday through a string of verbal abuses that he never wanted to see her again as long as he lived? Hell, that's what he said. I heard it all through the crack of his hospital room door. The article went on to say that Blanche was interviewed on the steps of the Baptist Hospital the afternoon before. The article further quoted Mrs. Blanche, "Earl was in great spirits, looking good, well enough to argue and it looks like we'll be able to reconcile our differences soon. You know you can't keep him down," she said.

God, I got to keep this paper away from Uncle Earl. Whatever happens, he can't see this story. It'll kill him for sure. I want to make sure no one brings him a paper and I need to warn Easy Money too, when he comes later tonight. Easy wouldn't know any better and can't read anyhow! So he'd show the Governor the paper by mistake, I thought. "Let me hide this paper. What time is it anyhow? I wondered.

It was around ten p.m. when Easy Money showed up at the hospital. After he gave the Governor a briefing about the cows and other livestock, I eased him out into the hall to tell him about the newspaper article. I warned him, after reading the article to him, not to let the Governor see the paper at any cost. It was the only time I ever lied to the Governor. When he had inquired about the paper earlier, I told him they were sold out and I couldn't find a paper. I was glad that he never insisted on having one. He loved to read and I gave him some magazines we had lying around the room. That seemed to appease him.

Before entering the hospital, the Governor had smoked three to four packs of unfiltered Lucky Strike cigarettes per day. Nearly everyone around him, including me, smoked. However, since he had been in the hospital, I smoked in the hallways, and he seemed to have lost his desire for the Lucky Strikes. I had discouraged him from smoking, as they made him cough. When he started coughing, hacking and gagging, I knew that it put too much of a strain on his heart. Maybe that big brown capsule had curbed his desire to smoke. Whatever, he was looking stronger this Sunday, even though he was still physically weak. I still had to rub his legs every two or three hours. His coughing had all but disappeared.

The bells somewhere tolled midnight and the Governor was awake. He seemed to want to talk to me and Easy Money about all kinds of mundane things. We quipped back and forth about hunting, dogs, fast women, whiskey and horses. He kept insisting that I take off and go home to rest up and spend a little time with my family. He insisted he'd be all right there with Easy Money to look after him. Tomorrow was Monday with not too much to do, he said. Besides, he was feeling much better and would be all right, he ventured. I hedged and kept hanging around. When the troubling starts in your soul, you just can't put your finger on it. I didn't know if it was duty, loyalty or I was just mesmerized from being there so long, but something deep inside said, "Don't go."

"You know I'm hungry," he said. "Jay, you go and see if they've got something to eat," he declared emphatically.

"Yes sir," I replied, looking at my watch. It was twelve thirty a.m. "What am I going to find this time of night?" I thought as I hurried down to the nurses' station.

"Well, we got some crackers and I could heat up a can of vegetable soup. That's about all we have," the nurse stated.

"That'll do. Matter-of-fact, that's great," I responded. That really sounded good to me and I was relieved to have found such a hearty snack so quickly.

As I sat by the Governor's bed, spooning the hot vegetable soup into his mouth, he seemed just a little lethargic and weak to me. His face pale and sallow, his leathery facial skin had faint stubble of beard and tomorrow he'll need shaving, I thought. I'd been shaving him everyday with a big old double-edged Gillette razor. I guess Easy would shave him in the morning. I would remind him before I left. The soup must have tasted good to the Governor, as he would close his eyes between bites and seem to savor the flavor. His false teeth were in a glass of water by the bed. He was gumming those saltine crackers with a delicate deliberateness that one does when one's false teeth are somewhere else, I thought. As I looked into those always questioning steel blue eyes, I wondered should I go home or stay. It would be the last time; I would physically do anything for the Governor.

"That's enough," he said pushing the spoon away from his lips. "You might as well go on home," he urged. "Me and Easy Money can make the rest of the night. Besides, you need to see your wife and that pretty little girl of yours."

"Yes sir, I guess you're right," I said.

"Of course, I am," he retorted. "See you tomorrow," As I backed out of the room, I saw Easy Money already stretching out on the day bed next to the door. Everything seemed peaceful enough as the Governor rolled over on his side and turned the reading light out that was snapped to the head of the bed. The small light switch chain was barely swinging on the light as the Governor signed, breathed deeply and settled in for the night.

"See ya, Easy. Goodnight," I whispered as I pulled the door closed on my last vision of Earl K. Long alive!

Day XI
"Monday"

It was getting close to two thirty a.m. when I slipped between the clean fresh covers of my old familiar bed in the back room of my mother and father's house. There was a gentle breeze blowing through the tops of the big tall pine trees right outside of my window. I didn't need any piney woods lullaby to put me to sleep. I crashed instantly into the blackness and deepest depths of sleep, lost to the world of politics, fast cars, fast women, Country music prestige and the future power of Washington, D.C.

"Wake up, wake up, Jay, wake up." Where was that distant, familiar voice coming from? Wherever it came from, there was an urgent cry on the lips of its sender. "You've got to wake up. Earl's dead. It just came on the TV news," my mother's voice slammed into my fully awakened brain like a load of double-ought buck shots from a .12 gauge shotgun.

"What! Are you sure? Oh shit! Where's my pants, my gun. . . I need a shirt. What else did the news say?" I shouted, fully alert and ready to kill someone, anyone, everyone. . . who? I thought as my mind raced like a speeding bullet, heading for an elusive, invisible target.

"Here's a cup of coffee," my mother said, as I darted for the door, half-dressed and half out of my mind.

"Thanks," I said.

"Be careful, son," she replied. "What are we going to do without Uncle Earl?" she went on. Her hands nervously wringing the edges of her apron, as I backed out of the driveway, spraying the dirt and gravel from behind my already racing automobile toward Alexandria and a date with death.

There's just something about Monday mornings in a hospital that is both sterile, clean and too damned business like to suit me! Stern, uncaring faces seemed to move back and forth automatically in the hallways, as I rushed up to the third floor and raced toward the Governor's room that I'd just left eight hours before, hoping against hope to find him still there. An empty hospital room, so neatly arranged after someone had just died, is the worst greeting in the world. My knees buckled and my stomach went nauseous. I rushed to the closet. The old aluminum suicase, clothes, whiskey, wine, the new will and little black book. . . all gone! The day bed where I'd slept for the last nine days. . . gone. There were clean, fresh sheets on his bed, but worst of all, Earl was gone. Now I really knew for the first time exactly how Scarlet felt in "Gone with the Wind" as I staggered backwards into the hall and headed for the elevator.

As the doors opened on the first floor, there stood Dr. Parrott by the nurses' station. Thank God, someone to talk to, I thought. "Dr. Parrott, Dr. Parrott," I hailed from this short distance.

"Yes, Jay," he said looking up from his clipboard.

"What happened?" I cried out. "When I left here last night he was perfectly all right. What happened?" I repeated with a controlled urgency in my voice.

"He had a massive heart attack this morning about six a.m.," he replied.

"Where was Easy Money?" I half shouted.

"He was there. . . said he was shaving. . .said the Governor was eating a candy bar and smoking a cigarette when it happened," the doctor went on.

"We held an autopsy. Would you like to see it?" he declared matter-of-factly. It sounded so routine that before I could reason in my mind, my lips agreed. "Follow me," he said.

It was my first time in a hospital laboratory and it smelled exactly like the chemical lab in high school. God, I hated the smell of these chemicals! He walked over to a long black counter where two jugs of formaldehyde stood. Contained in one, there was a set of human lungs, and in the other, a human heart.

"Well, you can see what the years of smoking the old Lucky Strike cigarettes did to his lungs," he said. I stared in horrified disbelief at a mass of blue, black looking lungs that had, a few moments ago, belonged to the Governor. "Over here in this jar is his heart," the doctor calmly stated as he slipped on a pair of rubber gloves and reached for a pencil in his pocket.

He reached into the jar of formaldehyde and retrieved the heart of the only man I'd ever loved besides my daddy and Jesus. "Right here, you can see this little fine line of scar tissue? This is the heart attack he had in 1950," he said as he traced the line with the end of his sharpened lead pencil. "Now here is the line that represents the beginning to form scar tissue from Friday was a week ago's heart attack." He moved the pencil slightly. "And here's the blowout he had this morning. . . the one that killed him. . . he didn't stand a chance. . . he's lucky he lived this long!" the doctor said. My mind reeled inward, and the tears flowed backwards burning my heart and numbing my body from head to toe.

"Thank you, Dr. Parrott," I mumbled as I moved to escape the awful stench of formaldehyde that would remain in my nostrils for the rest of my life. This moment would be forever ingrained in every cell of my mind and body. A tiny little triangle flap in the heart of Uncle Earl, looking like a small blowout on a bicycle inner tube, had stopped him cold! I stumbled out of the lab, looking for a place to wretch my guts out. I silently cursed fate, Blanche, politicians, people, doctors and the worst luck any man could have!

As I left the bathroom of the Baptist Hospital and slipped out into the September sunlight, I knew that Louisiana, home and Jay Chevalier would never be the same. I had just been kicked in the gut! Worse than that, the Eighth District, Louisiana and the people who had voted for Uncle Earl had just lost the "Best friend the poor white men and black man ever had!" Yep, like it or not, "The Last of the Red Hot Papas" was gone! Tricked by fate, cheated by the damn devil, hell and death itself. There is no justice in this world, I thought. The only plea you got is for mercy itself and I was in no pleading mood. Somewhere, somehow, sometime, I'll ride that wheel of fortune back around and make things right for ole Uncle Earl, I vowed.

Somewhere, a lonesome train whistle blew, as I slipped into the front seat of my blue and white 1959 Ford. I turned on the radio. The announcer said that the Governor's body would lay in state at the rotunda of the Capitol in Baton Rouge for a viewing; in much the same manner as Huey's had.

As I headed for Forest Hill, I knew I wasn't going to Baton Rouge, Winnfield or any place else for Earl's funeral. Hell, his heart was in a jug of formaldehyde at the Baptist Hospital. By god, that's all a man's got anyhow. . . his heart and spirit. So I ain't gonna go and see 'em put no body in the ground. He's got to go to heaven. He's done too much good for little children, oprhans, widows, poor blacks, whites and people of all walks of life. Earl's spirit. . . Hell, his spirit's all over Louisiana. . . I can hear it and feel it in the wind, I thought as I rolled the car window down. You can't bottle a man's spirit, you can't bury it either. Once it's loose, it's loose. It was on the wind, and by God, I'm going to follow the wind just as far as I can! That's it. . . I'm in the wind, friend.

"LOST IN LOUISIANA 1959"

I got lost in Louisiana in 1959
Between Hank Williams
And Ponchatoula, Louisiana Strawberry Wine
I got a hooked on a feelin' that's
Kept me reelin' deep down in my mind
I got lost in Louisiana in 1959.

The Big Bopper was a boppin'
In Beaumont in '59
Elvis was a Rockin' and knockin'
Everybody off the charts in '59
Well they hooked us on a feelin'
That's kept us all a reelin'
Deep down in our minds
And I got lost in Louisiana in 1959

Fat's Domino was a walkin'
To New Orleans in '59
Johnny Horton was recordin'
And Cash was a walkin' the line
Well they hooked us on a feelin'
That's kept us all a reelin'
Deep down in our minds and
I got lost in Louisiana in 1959

Blaze Starr was strippin' in
New Orleans in '59
Uncle Earl caught her fever
And he almost lost his mind
Well they hooked us on a feelin'
That's kept us all a reelin'
Deep down in our minds
'I got lost in Louisiana in 1959

Loretta Lynn was a coal
Miner's daughter in '59
She loved Ernest and Hank
And she was "Crazy" 'bout Patsy Cline
Well they hooked us on a feelin'
That's kept us all a reelin'
Deep down in our minds
'I got lost in Louisiana in 1959

Between Hank Williams
And Ponchatoula, Louisiana Strawberry Wine
I got a hooked on a feelin'
That's a kept me reelin'
Deep down in my mind
'I got lost in Louisiana in 1959

I got lost in Louisiana in 1959

Words and Music by:
Jay Chevalier
© Jay Chevalier Music BMI

"BLAZE"

The first time I met her I felt a fever coming over me
Like a Louisiana wind blowing wild, hot, Louisiana heat
She swung and she swayed as I stood there amazed
    at this lady and all she displayed.
I wanted to holler, throw down my last dollar
And I guess that's why they call the lady "Blaze."

The next time I met her the fever turned into a fire
Consuming my heart and my soul with a burning desire.
They said I was crazy to let such a lady
    set my poor heart in a whirl
But the fire she had started burned down in my heart
And ignited the rest of my world.

They call the lady "Blaze" as she burned on thru the night
On that Bourbon Street corner I was a Long gonner
And I guess that's why they call the lady "Blaze."

The last time I saw her she held me so close to her breast
With a whisper consoled me as I drew my very last breath
She told me she loved me held no one above me
    leaned down and kissed me goodbye
The light that I left her is burning forever
A blazing love that never ever died.

They call the lady "Blaze" as she burned on thru the night
On that Bourbon Street corner I was a Long gonner
And I guess that's why they call the lady "Blaze."

Written by: Jay Chevalier,
Shelley Ford, Cid Zane Chevalier
©1989 Jay Chevalier Music, BMI

"THE BALLAD OF EARL K.LONG"

CHORUS: *Sing, Sing, Louisiana Sing, Sing about the Battle of New Orleans*
Clap your hands, and sing your song, just a little story 'bout
Earl K. Long

Talk about your Jackson, your Robert E. Lee
Sing about Davey from Ole Tennessee
But way down south in the Bayou land
A modern Robin Hood is a' leadin' his clan

REPEAT CHORUS

Drivin' around in a big limousine
Everywhere he goes, there's a great big scene
All of the folks come from miles around
Just to see the show when he hits town

REPEAT CHORUS

Drivin' around, settin' the state in a whirl
Sayin, "Don't ya worry, just trust Uncle Earl,"
Climb on the wagon and grab yourself a hat
We'll all take a trip out to his Pea Patch

REPEAT CHORUS

Well, some say he's wrong and others, not so
The rest of the people, just don't know
But to this one thing we'll all agree
Ole Uncle Earl has made history

REPEAT CHORUS

Words and Music by Jay Chevalier
©1959

"A CAJUN TOAST TO YOU MY FRIEND"

CHORUS: *A Cajun toast to you my friend*
A Cajun toast to the end
Best wishes mon a mie
And love to my cherie

May there be crawfish in your nets
And gumbo in your pot.
May the Sac-au-lait be biting
At your favorite fishing spot.

May the sun shine brightly
A when you need its cheerful rays.
May the oak tree shade you gently
On those lazy bayou days

May a Bourree game be waiting
When all your work is through.
May the fais-do-do bring pretty girls
To toss a wink at you.

And when your time is over
And your place on earth is gone,
May you waltz right into heaven
To the tune of "Jolie Blonde."

REPEAT CHORUS

"IN THE GARDEN"*

I come to the garden alone,
While the dew is still on the roses,
And the voice I hear, Falling on my ear,
The Son of God discloses.

And He walks with me, and He talks with me,
And He tells me I am His own;
And the joy we share as we tarry there,
None other has ever known.

He speaks, and the sound of His voice
Is so sweet the birds hush their singing,
And the melody that He gave to me,
Within my heart is ringing.

And He walks with me, and He talks with me,
And He tells me I am His own;
And the joy we share as we tarry there,
None other has ever known.

I'd stay in the garden with Him
Tho' the night around me be falling,
But He bids me go; Thro' the voice of woe
His voice to me is calling.

And He walks with me, and He talks with me,
And He tells me I am His own;
And the joy we share as we tarry there,
None other has ever known.

This was Earl Long's favorite hymn and the verses are carved on his tomb in Winnfield, Louisiana.

Rodeheaver Volume Courtesy of Ethel Lea Peters, Winnfield, Louisiana

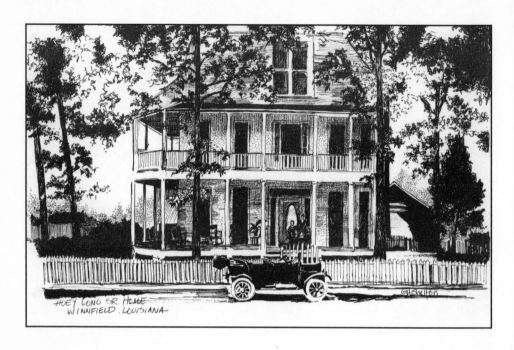

HUEY LONG SR. HOME
WINNFIELD, LOUISIANA

EARL LONG'S PEA PATCH FARM,
WINNFIELD, LOUISIANA
58/100

Photographs from the movie, "Blaze."

170